MS
SURGERY | 6 | Mast

MW00575324

Series Editor:
Dana K. Andersen, MD

Advance *noun*...progress, improvement, movement toward a goal.

Each volume in the Master Series in Surgery *will provide a comprehensive review of current advances in a major area of surgery. The objective is to provide the reader with practical, up-to-date information and to favor the clinical more than the experimental aspect of the topics presented. However, special attention will be devoted to the discussion of recent investigative findings that might impact the conduct of surgical and clinical practices in these areas. The volumes of the series are not intended to serve as "how-to" books, but as useful references by authorities in the field.*

Series Editor: Dana K. Andersen, MD

Advances in Surgical Gene Therapy

Volume 6
Master Series in Surgery

Series Editor: Dana K. Andersen, MD
Professor of Surgery
Chief, Surgical Gastroenterology
Yale University School of Medicine

 WORLD MEDICAL PRESS

Library of Congress Cataloging in Publication Data
Main entry under title:
Advances in Surgical Gene Therapy
(Master Series in Surgery)
Includes bibliographies and index.

©1994 World Medical Press
Division, World Medical Communications Organization.

Printed in the United States of America

ISBN 0-933751-09-5 World Medical Press

Preface

TO VOLUME 6

As we stand on the brink of the 21st century we can see what medicine and surgery will look like in the coming years: Operative procedures performed through finger-size incisions, wounds healing without infection or scar, and diseases reversed by the transplantation of cells rather than organs, and genes rather than cells. Gene therapy was little more than a dream just 5 years ago. Now surgeons are helping to develop this new modality, and this volume of *Master Series in Surgery* outlines the state of the art in this rapidly emerging field.

The basic concept of gene therapy is providing a therapeutic gene by an appropriate delivery vehicle to transform a defective or untreated cell to a "normal" cell or a cell that is capable of producing a normal product. *Ex vivo* gene therapy refers to the process whereby target tissues or cells are removed, gene transduction is performed, and the cells are reimplanted. *In vivo* therapy refers to the in situ transduction of target cells with the therapeutic gene. The selection of an appropriate delivery vehicle for the introduction of a therapeutic gene is an important and largely unresolved issue. Liposomes (lipid envelopes containing a DNA sequence), retroviruses (RNA-containing viruses that require target tissues to be in an actively dividing state), and adenoviruses, which penetrate quiescent cells but may evoke an immune response that limits their efficacy, are among the potential vectors for gene therapy of specific disorders. Current concerns in gene therapy are directed at problems such as tissue penetration and efficiency of transfection, specificity and durability (permanence) of gene transfer, effects of transfection on nontarget or adjacent cells, host response, and safety of viral vectors. Despite many questions that remain unanswered, over 80 protocols in seven countries have been established, and over 300 patients have been treated for a wide variety of diseases.

There is a temptation to think of gene therapy as someone else's business, but surgeons are already applying these methods to treat patients with gastrointestinal disease, vascular disease, and malignancies, and will rely on these new techniques to manage those aspects of these diseases that previously were beyond our ability to control. The mastery of these molecular approaches requires a new body of knowledge and a new lexicon. Ex vivo gene therapy, with its strong dependence on traditional surgical techniques, suicide genes, and retroviral vectors, must become as familiar to us as absorbable sutures, cytokines, and laparoscopy. The reading may be hard-going at times, but by the end of this volume the image of medicine and surgery in the 21st century will be clearer for you than it ever has been.

In his section on general principles and applications of gene therapy to gastrointestinal disorders, Dr Steven Raper describes how the removal and transformation of autologous tissue can reverse a metabolic disease. He guides us through a discussion of the possible vectors that can be used to replace defective or absent genetic information, and outlines the concepts behind the various molecular approaches to these diseases. Inherited gastrointestinal disorders that have been targeted for gene therapy, including familial hypercholesterolemia, the pancreatic manifestations of cystic fibrosis, and congenital hyperbilirubinemia caused by bilirubin glucuronosyltransferase deficiency or Crigler-Najjar syndrome type I, are reviewed, and the results of the latest studies are discussed.

In their section on gene therapy of vascular diseases, Dr Louis Messina and his colleagues review the applications of these methods, which have been directed at problems such as the patency of vascular conduits and the management of underlying vascular diseases. The authors review the successes, limitations, and potential approaches for gene therapy targeted to large-vessel and capillary endothelium, and to vascular smooth muscle cells. The development of cell-mediated (ex vivo) gene transfer techniques and some novel, catheter-assisted methods of direct gene transfer to vascular cells are also discussed.

Finally, in the section on gene therapy of malignant disorders, Drs Economou and Toloza describe how malignant diseases are already being managed with gene therapy. They provide a primer of the various strategies already in use or under development for the transformation of malignant cells and the successful elimination of disseminated or metastatic tumors. Antisense therapy, in which an activated oncogene or effector protein is neutralized; tumor suppressor gene therapy; suicide gene therapy, where an enzyme is encoded that converts a nontoxic drug to a cytotoxic compound to effect tumor cell death; and cytokine and antigen gene therapy are reviewed as methods to selectively kill malignant cells.

Interestingly, the editors of this volume all received their general surgery training at the University of California, San Francisco. Their subsequent careers have established them as leaders in the applications of molecular biology and academic surgery, and each of these sections provides an extraordinary glimpse of strategies that have translated discoveries in molecular biology to the treatment of clinical disorders. It is applied science in the highest sense.

Steven E. Raper, MD, is Associate Professor of Surgery at the University of Pennsylvania. He is an investigator at the Institute for Human Gene Therapy in Philadelphia, and recently won international acclaim for his role in the treatment of the inherited hepatocellular disease, familial hypercholesterolemia.

Louis M. Messina, MD, is Associate Professor of Surgery in the Section of Vascular Surgery at the University of Michigan, Ann Arbor. He and his colleagues have been leaders in the application of molecular methods to the treatment of vascular diseases and the development of genetically altered vascular conduits.

James S. Economou, MD, PhD, is the Beaumont Professor of Surgery in the Section of Surgical Oncology at the University of California, Los Angeles. His laboratory has been at the forefront of new applications of gene transfer in the treatment of malignant diseases.

Dana K. Andersen, MD

Contributors

Series Editor:

Dana K. Andersen, MD
Professor of Surgery
Chief, Surgical Gastroenterology
Yale University School of Medicine

Volume Editors:

Steven E. Raper, MD
Associate Professor of Surgery
University of Pennsylvania
Institute for Human Gene Therapy

Louis M. Messina, MD
Associate Professor of Surgery
University of Michigan–Ann Arbor

James S. Economou, MD, PhD
Beaumont Professor of Surgery
University of California–Los Angeles

Contents

I Gene Therapy in the Gastrointestinal Tract

Steven E. Raper, MD

INTRODUCTION

The new disciplines of molecular medicine and gene therapy promise to revolutionize the practice of medicine. Although only a fraction of the human genome has been cloned, sequenced, and mapped to individual chromosomes, clinical gene therapy protocols have been approved and experiments are being performed. The regulatory process leading to the approval of these protocols is arduous, and has been developed to ensure maximum safety of experimental subjects. Although many gene therapy protocols have been directed toward the hematopoietic system, the liver has served as a target organ for the first trial of ex vivo human gene therapy for familial hypercholesterolemia (FH). The low rate of gene transfer associated with retroviral transduction has led to the search for vectors with a higher level of gene transfer efficiency. Recombinant adenoviruses appear most promising, but adeno-associated viruses (AAVs), liposomes, DNA-protein complexes, and other viruses are being evaluated. With regard to the gastrointestinal tract, gene therapy strategies are being considered for diabetes mellitus, FH, ornithine-transcarbamylase (OTC) deficiency, Crigler-Najjar syndrome type I, the pancreaticobiliary manifestations of cystic fibrosis (CF), cancer, and the immunomodulation of allografts to prevent rejection. As genes are identified, other diseases will become candidates for gene therapy in the next few years.

Current indications for gastrointestinal gene therapy

THE HUMAN GENOME PROJECT AND GENE THERAPY

The U. S. Human Genome Project has been organized to assist in an international effort to sequence the human genome (genetic material). The first goal, which should be achieved by 1995, was to develop a genetic map of the entire human genome accurate to within 2 to 5 centiMorgans (cM; a unit of genetic distance between two locations on a chromosome with a 1% chance of recombination in a given meiotic event).[1] By 1998, investigators hope to have a physical map with a resolution of 100 kilobases (kb; 1 kb = 1,000 nucleotide base pairs). Next, a complete sequence of the entire genome using this physical map is predicted for the year 2005. Lastly, all genes contained in the human genome will be identified, a process for which the end is not yet in sight. How many genes does the human genome contain? If one defines a gene as a distinct transcription unit that may be translated into one or a set of related proteins, one recent estimate sets the number of genes at 60,000 to 70,000.[2]

Project targets and dates

Other goals are also planned for the U. S. Human Genome Project, including the development of informatics and sequencing technology, analysis of the ethical, social, and legal implications of the information generated, and training of new investigators. The project has already spawned the concept of molecular medicine, and had a major impact on biomedical research. Genes associated with Huntington's disease, neurofibromatosis, amyotrophic lateral sclerosis, myotonic dystrophy, and the fragile X syndrome have been identified. Genes associated with more common diseases, such as colon and breast cancer, hypertension, diabetes mellitus, and Alzheimer's disease also have been found. It is the constant identification of genes causing illness that has led to the feasibility of genetic correction of disease: gene therapy.

Other goals

GENERAL APPROACHES TO GENE THERAPY

The development of a gene therapy protocol requires an understanding of the defective gene, the biology of target cells, the pathobiology of the disease, and a complete command of the available technology. Two general strategies are considered when planning somatic gene therapy–based treatment. The most popular approach, which has been used in the first human trials, is referred to as ex vivo gene therapy. Ex vivo gene therapy involves the transplantation of genetically modified autologous cells. Tissue that contains the appropriate target cell is harvested from the patient. A variety of somatic cells have been studied for somatic gene transfer, including hematopoietic stem cells,[3] hepatocytes,[4] respiratory airway epithelial cells,[5] lymphocytes,[6,7] endothelial cells,[8] myocytes,[9,10] fibroblasts,[11] synovium,[12] and brain cells.[13] Recombinant retroviruses have been the preferred substrate for transducing genes into dividing cells in vitro.[14] The genetically modified cells are harvested and transplanted back into the patient from whom they were derived. Two advantages to this approach are that gene transfer can be accomplished efficiently in vitro and the genetically modified cells can be characterized prior to transplantation. Ex vivo gene therapy generally

Ex vivo gene therapy

requires two invasive procedures, target cell harvest and genetically altered cell reinfusion. The efficacy of ex vivo gene therapy is dependent on the number of cells that can be harvested, and the titer and efficiency of infection of the target cells by the chosen vector (eg, recombinant virus, liposome).

In vivo gene therapy

A potentially more efficient approach to gene therapy is direct delivery of the therapeutic genes to cells in vivo. This would require the development of gene transfer vectors capable of targeting only the correct cell type and transport of the gene to the nucleus where it is expressed. An equally wide array of gene transfer substrates are available. Approaches for in vivo gene transfer include adenoviruses,[15,16] AAVs,[17] herpes simplex virus,[13] and nonviral substrates, such as liposomes[18,19] and DNA-protein complexes.[20]

RETROVIRUSES

Figure 1

Retroviral vectors have been used for a number of active trials of ex vivo gene transfer to mark cells as well as to treat diseases. Retrovirus particles are composed of an RNA genome encapsulated into a complex virus particle structure containing viral and cellular components (Fig. 1). The virus enters cells primarily through interactions between the viral envelope protein and specific proteins on the recipient cell membrane.[21] Once internalized, the viral RNA is converted to a double-stranded DNA sequence (provirus) and the proviral DNA is integrated into the host chromosome by means of an integrase protein utilizing proviral DNA sequences known as long terminal repeats.[22] An important point is the need for host cell replication to accomplish proviral DNA integration.[23]

Efficient gene therapy

The ability to accomplish two of the most important functions necessary for efficient gene transfer, entry into cells and integration of genes in a stable and heritable fashion, make retroviruses good gene transfer substrates. Progress in adapting retroviruses for use in gene transfer has been made primarily with mouse viruses. Mouse retroviruses are classified on the basis of the cells they infect. Ecotropic viruses infect rodent cells whereas amphotropic viruses are hosted by a wide range of cell types, including many human cells.

Viruses that express the therapeutic gene

Replication-deficient retroviral vectors suitable for gene therapy are produced by introducing several mutated DNA sequences into a packaging cell line, such as the mouse lymphocyte line NIH 3T3. One DNA sequence expresses proteins necessary to assemble a virus particle while another DNA sequence can be transcribed into RNA molecules specific for the therapeutic gene of interest. The packaging cell line produces viruses that contain only RNA encoding information for the desired therapeutic protein, not potentially harmful viruses. The only viruses that are exported from the packaging cell are those that will express the therapeutic gene, and are capable of directing the target cell to synthesize only the protein of interest.

Possible limits of retrovirus gene therapy

However, there are several limitations of recombinant retroviruses that make them unsuitable for all gene transfer protocols. First, retrovirus entry requires that target cells contain

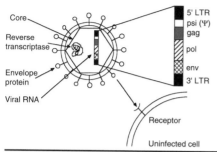

Fig. 1A. Steps involved in the construction of a retroviral vector. A schematic representation of the key features of a retroviral particle. Envelope proteins are important in binding and uptake of the virus into the host cell. Viral reverse transcriptase allows conversion of viral to a DNA provirus. The long terminal repeats (LTRs) are essential for viral integration. The ψ sequence is necessary for packaging of RNA molecules into virions prior to budding from the host cell membrane. (From Raper SE, Wilson JM. *Cell Transplantation* 1993;2:381-400. Reprinted with permission.)

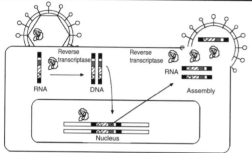

Fig. 1B. Lifecycle of a retrovirus. The envelope glycoproteins bind to specific cell surface proteins and fuse with the cell membrane, allowing entry of virion particles. Once in the cell, molecules of viral reverse transcriptase are packaged into the virus in an active form, convert RNA to DNA. Proviral DNA integrates randomly into the genome of the proliferating host cell. Retroviral progeny are synthesized using host cell mechanisms, and packaging of infectious RNA requires ψ sequences. (From Raper SE, Wilson JM. *Cell Transplantation* 1993;2:381-400. Reprinted with permission.)

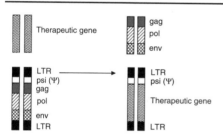

Fig. 1C. Construction of therapeutic proviral DNA. Using standard DNA cloning techniques, it is possible to substitute a therapeutic gene, along with desired promoters, enhancers, and selectable markers for endogenous retroviral structural sequences. By making the therapeutic DNA provirus ψ+, subsequent therapeutic RNA molecules can be selectively packaged. (From Raper SE, Wilson JM. *Cell Transplantation* 1993;2:381-400. Reprinted with permission.)

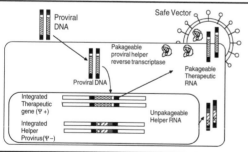

Fig. 1D. Creation of a packaging cell line. Transduction of newly synthesized therapeutic proviral DNA can be accomplished by any of a number of methods for the introduction of foreign DNA. Packaging cells also must contain an integrated helper provirus, containing all necessary structural sequences, but excluding the ψ sequences, so that only RNA molecules containing the therapeutic sequences can be exported. The usual titer of therapeutic proviral particles is on the order of 10^5 to 10^6/mL media. (From Raper SE, Wilson JM. *Cell Transplantation* 1993;2:381-400. Reprinted with permission.)

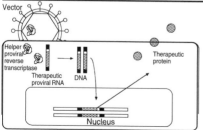

Fig. 1E. Infection of target cells. By harvesting media from cultured packaging cells, retroviral vectors containing only therapeutic RNA are obtained. Introduction of this media into cultures of target cells (ie, hepatocytes) allows infection and production of only the desired therapeutic protein. No infectious progeny are produced, adding to the safety of this form of therapy. (From Raper SE, Wilson JM. *Cell Transplantation* 1993;2:381-400. Reprinted with permission.)

the appropriate viral receptor. In many cases these receptors are not known. This fact has led to the development of various host-range retrovirus packaging cells lines.[24] Thus, difficulties in efficiently transducing certain target cell populations may be due to low-level or absent receptors. A second requirement for efficient retroviral gene integration and expression is cell proliferation. In rodent cells infected with Moloney murine leukemia virus (MLV), the integration of viral DNA and the production of viral proteins occurred only after the cells went through mitosis, and integration was blocked when the cells were prevented from progressing through mitosis.[25] Thus, the dependence of integration on mitosis may be due to a requirement for mitosis and nuclear envelope breakdown for entry of the viral integration complex into the nucleus. Whether breakdown of the nuclear envelope is required for other recombinant viruses is still a matter of conjecture. Production is another problem. Retrovirus particles are relatively labile compared with other viruses, such as adenoviruses. In general, retrovirus cannot be purified without significant loss of infectivity. Titers of infectious retrovirus tend to be in the range of 10^6 to 10^7 particles/mL; five to six logs lower that that of adenoviruses.

ADENOVIRUSES

Recombinant adenoviruses represent an important technology for the development of in vivo gene therapy for the pulmonary manifestations of CF.[26] First-generation recombinant adenoviruses with deletions of sequences that encode for proteins that regulate the viral life cycle have been useful in demonstrating the principle of liver-directed gene therapy of the biliary manifestations of CF in vivo.[27] However, in rodent models expression of the recombinant gene is transient and associated with the development of inflammation. Second-generation adenoviruses, which have been further crippled by ablating other early viral genes, may be useful in circumventing the problems encountered in first-generation adenoviruses by avoiding destructive cellular immune responses.

Human adenoviruses are comprised of a 36-kb double-stranded DNA genome that undergoes a highly regulated program of gene expression during its normal viral life cycle.[28] The genomic organization of human type C adenovirus, which includes the two most common serotypes used for gene therapy expression vectors, Ad 5 and Ad 2, is presented in Fig. 2.

Figure 2

At least 40 human adenovirus serotypes cause a variety of nonlethal diseases, including hepatitis, conjunctivitis, upper respiratory tract infection, and diarrhea.[29] Many episodes of the common cold that we encounter in childhood are the result of adenoviral infections. Multiple exposure to adenoviruses throughout life results in a variable profile of preexisting humoral immunities. Adenoviruses are internalized by receptor-mediated endocytosis (the exact receptor has not been determined) and transported to the nucleus where the immediate early genes, E1a and E1b, are expressed. The products of these genes regulate the expression of a variety of host genes and activate the expression of the early delayed genes, which include E2, E3, and E4. Early genes express a variety of proteins involved in the regulation of gene expression and control of the viral life cycle. The concerted activities of these early genes contribute to the initiation of the late phase of viral replication whose hallmark is the onset of DNA replication and activation of expression from a major late promoter (MLP). A large mRNA produced from this MLP undergoes extensive posttranscriptional processing, leading to expression of five sets of late proteins (L1 through L5) that are structural

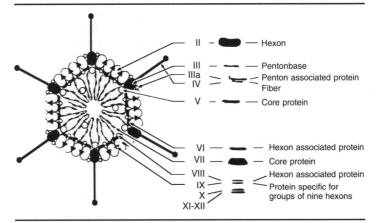

Fig. 2A. Schematic representation of an adenovirus. The mobilities and relative amounts of each protein after electrophoresis of the dissociated virus on a sodium dodecyl sulfate-containing polyacrylamide gel are shown on the right. The position of each polypeptide in the virion is designated; however, the configuration of the DNA does not imply the actual structure within the core. The roman numerals refer to a polypeptide designation described by Maizel JV Jr, et al (*Virology* 1968;36:126-136). The hexon (II), penton base (III), fiber (IV), and hexon-associated proteins (IIIa, VI, VIII, and IX) are subunits of the capsid. The core contains proteins V, VII, and u, as well as the 55-kd terminal protein covalently linked to each of the 5' ends of the linear DNA. The two molecules of TP per virion are too few to be demonstrated by the Coomassie stain of the viral polypeptides, and u probably is one of the polypeptides found in the region of the gel-containing proteins X to XII. (From Persson H, Phillips L. *Curr Top Microbiol Immunol* 1982;97:157-203. Reprinted with permission.)

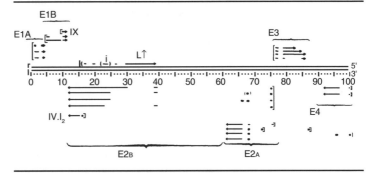

Fig. 2B. Genomic map of Ad 2–coded early proteins and their mRNAs. The mRNAs (thin lines) can be detected at early times postinfection in the absence of protein synthesis. Thick lines indicate intermediate mRNAs that can be expressed in the absence of viral DNA replication, but they are most easily detected at late times. Arrowheads show the 3' end. Tentative promoter sites are indicated by [–. (From Persson H, Phillips L. *Curr Top Microbiol Immunol* 1982;97:157-203. Modified with permission.)

components of the virion.

The initial strategy for the development of recombinant adenoviruses for gene therapy was based on the premise that deleting E1 should render the recombinant virus replication defective. First-generation recombinant adenoviruses deleted in E1 can be propagated in vitro in 293 cells, a human embryonic kidney cell that stably expresses E1a and E1b.[30] The versatility of first-generation recombinant adenoviruses for in vivo gene therapy has been demonstrated in multiple systems. The virus can be grown in large quantities and highly purified; administration of the virus in vivo has been associated with high-level expression in several biologic settings.[31] Injection of first-generation recombinant adenovirus into the portal or peripheral circulation of a variety of animals, including mice, cotton rats, rabbits, and nonhuman primates, leads to high-level recombinant gene expression in the majority of hepatocytes. The expression of viral proteins leads to cellular immune responses to the genetically modified cells, which results in their destruction and replacement of the organ with non–transgene-containing cells. One strategy to improve transgene stability is further crippling the adenovirus so as to minimize expression of the remaining viral genes. This should improve the performance of these delivery vehicles.[32,33] Solving the problem of transient expression and tissue injury requires a complete understanding of the precise immunologic mechanisms elicited by first-generation recombinant adenoviruses. The recombinant viruses can then be engineered to subvert the immune system.

Problems with first-generation adenoviral vectors

ADENO-ASSOCIATED VIRUSES

Adeno-associated virus (AAV) is a human parvovirus that can propagate as a lytic infection or integrate into the host genome as a provirus. In general, AAV requires the presence of a helper, usually adenovirus, to initiate productive infection. Five serotypes of AAV have been identified, but AAV-2 is the most extensively characterized. Adeno-associated virus–2 DNA is a single-strand linear molecule approximately 4.7 kb in length.[34] Recently, an in-depth review of the life cycle of AAV has been published.[35] The integration of AAV is reportedly targeted to a site on the distal portion of the long arm of chromosome 19.[36]

These unique aspects of AAV have led to considerable interest in its use as a transduction vector. Although no AAV-mediated gene transfer has yet been shown in liver or pancreas, successful gene transfer with transduction frequencies as high as 80% has been demonstrated in human erythroid cells and lymphocytes.[6,17,37]

Packaging constraints limit the size of introduced sequences to approximately 4.7 kb; however, in the presence of adenovirus helper function, infectious AAV plasmids are able to transiently express much larger heterologous sequences.[38] Another potential advantage of AAV is the specific site of incorporation on chromosome 19, which would further decrease the risk of insertional mutagenesis from random integration.

DNA/PROTEIN COMPLEXES AND LIPOSOMES

Nonviral, noninfective gene therapy

A variety of strategies are being developed to accomplish gene transfer by noninfectious means, utilizing the lipid solubility of membranes or receptor-mediated endocytosis. The advantages of using a selective, physiologic pathway include specific targeting of a select cell population, a nontoxic means of entering the cell, and the ability to repeatedly administer a therapeutic gene. Although a number of studies are looking at the ability of DNA protein complexes to transfer genetic information in vivo, it is also possible to transfect cells in culture as a prelude to ex vivo therapy.

Despite the fact that DNA-protein complexes or liposome administration is associated with gene transfer efficiency similar to that seen with viral vectors, several problems remain to be solved. Liposomes appear to be safe in vivo, useful in a wide variety of cell types, and of relatively low cost.[39] However, two major disadvantages are the variability in production and the relative nonspecificity. A characteristic structure of liposomes is noted in

Figure 3

Fig. 3. The number of cell surface receptors that could be targeted by DNA-protein complexes is small, and for the liver would include the asialoglycoprotein and transferrin receptors, for which pathways responsible for the uptake of asialoglycoproteins and transferrin have been well worked out. A polypeptide ligand for the hepatocyte-specific asialoglycoprotein receptor,

Figure 4

asialoorosomucoid, has been conjugated to poly-(L-lysine) and mixed in vitro with a plasmid-based expression vector (Fig. 4).

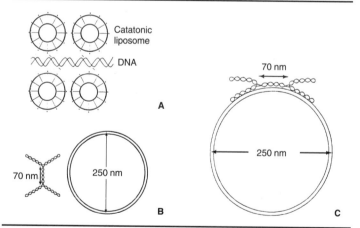

Fig. 3. The approximate structure in solution of the 250-nm diameter liposome and closed circular plasmid DNA used by Felgner and Ringold. (A) The electrostatic model of lipid–DNA complexes proposed by Felgner and Ringold (*Nature* 1989;337:387-388) to describe the DNA transfer efficiency of the cationic lipofection reagent lipofectin. Note, the DNA is shown linearized by these authors. (B) The true approximate structure in solution of the 2,500-bp closed circular plasmid used by Felgner and Ringold in relation to a 250-nm diameter liposome. Note the difference in size between the two particles. The plasmid structure would seem conducive to the formation of liposome tetramers. However, the accumulated positive charge densities of the liposomes would probably cause the closely associated liposomes to repel each other and disassociate from the DNA. (C) A model of the plasmid–DNA association, perhaps analogous to the situation in studies concerning the cationic liposomes such as lipofectin. (From Smith JG, et al.[39] Reprinted with permission.)

The DNA-protein complex could be internalized in a specific, saturable manner and transient gene expression noted.[20] This strategy was used to partially correct genetic analbuminemia in Nagase rats for up to 4 weeks.[40]

THE LIVER

A number of single-gene defects leading to inherited metabolic disease are known to primarily affect the liver or its secreted proteins.[41] The therapeutic efficacy of the correction of a single protein, such as the low-density lipoprotein receptor (LDL-R), was demonstrated through early attempts at gene therapy of metabolic disease by orthotopic liver transplantation.[42] When attempting ex vivo gene transfer, the ability to successfully resect significant quantities of liver and rely on regeneration to restore liver volume allows for the harvesting of adequate hepatocytes. A number of nonmetabolic diseases are also good candidates for liver-directed gene therapy. Primary and metastatic cancer, viral infection, and allograft rejection are more common problems than are the primary metabolic diseases, and are associated with a potentially greater impact on health care. The major drawback to gene therapy for nonmetabolic liver disease is the lack of suitable identified genes for treatment. It is unlikely that successful treatment would be based on the correction of one of the identified genetic defects underlying cancer, even if known, because of the need for complete killing. Viral infections, such as hepatitis B (HBV), may be amenable to antisense or ribozyme approaches to downregulate viral gene expression although such approaches

Gene therapy for nonmetabolic diseases

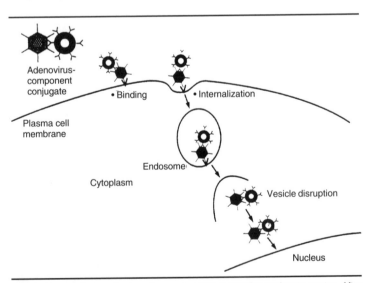

Fig. 4. Entry pathway of adenovirus-component molecular conjugate vector. After binding to target cells, the complex is internalized via the receptor-mediated endocytosis pathway. Escape from the endosome is accomplished by adenoviral-mediated disruption of the cell vesicle. This allows the complex to ingress into the cytosol, where it may access the nuclear pore based on adenoviral nuclear localization signals. (From Curiel DT, in Melnick JL [ed]. *Progress in Medical Virology.* Karger, Basel 1993, vol 40, p 1-18. Reprinted with permission.)

would not constitute gene therapy in the strictest sense. Current immunosuppressant regimens to prevent liver allograft rejection are not without risks. If the donor organ could be modified prior to transplantation, less systemic immunosuppression might be needed or could be eliminated entirely. In addition to allografts, xenografts could be used, as techniques to genetically modify histocompatibility antigens or introduce cytokine genes are developed.

EX VIVO LIVER-DIRECTED GENE THERAPY

Autologous vs allogenic hepatocytes for ex vivo gene transfer

One of the most important questions one confronts when considering the development of an ex vivo protocol is whether to use autologous or allogeneic hepatocytes. Autologous hepatocytes, or cells obtained from an afflicted individual, possess one significant advantage over allogeneic cells, or those obtained from a different donor: a lack of requirement for immunosuppression. The first human liver-directed ex vivo gene therapy trial utilized hepatocytes from the patients' own livers to avoid long-term immunosuppression. However, there are two major drawbacks to the use of autologous cells. One is the need for invasive surgical procedures to harvest an adequate numbers of cells. A patient already debilitated by an underlying genetic defect is therefore subjected to all of the risks of a major surgical procedure. The other drawback is that it may be possible to perform only a limited number of tissue harvest procedures without further increasing the risk of major morbidity and mortality or depleting the supply of cells to be transduced.

Providing rejection can be prevented, the use of allogeneic hepatocytes circumvents several problems. Surgical harvesting in the recipient is not necessary, and allogeneic cells provide a renewable resource for repeated treatments. In one study, isolated, cryopreserved human liver cells were attached to collagen-coated microcarriers and injected intraperitoneally into Gunn rats deficient in hepatic bilirubin uridine diphosphoglucuronosyl-transferase or Nagase analbuminemic rats. Subgroups of both rat strains were made immunodeficient by crossing them with athymic strains with an inherited T-cell deficiency. No histologic evidence of rejection was seen in the athymic rats, while immunocompetent rats did manifest evidence of rejection.[43] Furthermore, there was evidence of partial correction of both genetic defects.

The challenge of hepatocytes

Cultured hepatocytes provide several challenges as targets for retroviral-mediated gene transfer. Although it is possible to isolate relatively pure fractions of hepatocytes and establish primary cultures, hepatocytes are difficult to maintain for extended periods of time and are impossible to passage. Furthermore, hepatocytes begin to lose differentiated function within several days of isolation. Therefore, efficient transduction must be achieved by a single, relatively short exposure to virus soon after the cells are isolated.

RECOMBINANT RETROVIRUSES AS GENE TRANSFER SUBSTRATES FOR EX VIVO GENE THERAPY

For hepatocytes, the liver seems to provide the most physiologic

Quantity of hepatocytes for transfusion

site for transplantation. The extracellular matrix of the liver is most conducive to support of the hepatocyte, and only in the liver would hepatocytes be able to develop polarity and, potentially, secrete bile. In addition, the liver is the recipient of all portal venous blood. An important issue relates to the volume and number of cells to be infused. Based on hepatocyte transplantations performed, it is possible to harvest between 1 and 10×10^9 cells from a piece of liver that one can expect to obtain by removing the left lateral segment of a liver (weight, approximately 70 g) from a 4-year-old. Experience with the Watanabe heritable hyperlipidemic (WHHL) rabbit indicates that 2×10^8 cells can be safely transplanted into 2-kg animals. Therefore, it is reasonable to use 1×10^8 cells/kg in human studies, up to the maximum number of cells harvested. Considerations include the absolute volume to be infused which, in humans, may be as much as 50 to 180 mL. It is possible that overexpression of a therapeutic gene would allow a corresponding decrease in the number of reinfused cells necessary to achieve a therapeutic effect, but the volume infused would still be relatively large. Purified pancreatic islet suspensions, infused into the umbilical vein remnant, are on the order of only 2 to 3 mL.[44] In general, then, it is necessary to infuse relatively large volumes of hepatocyte suspensions. A high-flow system, such as the portal venous system, is best for uniform dissemination of cells into the liver.

Protocol for transduction of human hepatocytes

Gene transfer studies with recombinant retroviruses have been performed in hepatocytes from a variety of species. Using highly enriched populations of hepatocytes cultured from Sprague-Dawley rats, the β-galactosidase gene from *Escherichia coli* was efficiently and stably transduced into a retroviral vector. Presence of the gene, not found in mammalian cells, was demonstrated by histochemical staining and DNA (Southern blot) analysis.[4] An efficiency of infection of 25% was obtained, and analysis of the cultures revealed that 95% of the cells present in culture were hepatocytes. Similar results have been obtained by other investigators in rats, newborn and adult mice, newborn and adult rabbits, and baboons. Protocols for isolation worked out in the livers of other species are applicable to human hepatocytes, and procedures have been developed for the efficient transduction of primary cultures of human hepatocytes with retroviral vectors.[45] Gene transfer using a recombinant retrovirus containing the gene for the human LDL-R was also present, as documented by supranormal uptake of fluorescent-labeled LDL.[46]

Methods for hepatocyte reinfusion into portal vein system

Our preferred approach to hepatocyte transplantation is the direct reinfusion of autologous human hepatocytes into a tributary of the portal venous system. There are benefits as well as drawbacks to this approach. The ability to leave an indwelling Hickman-type catheter at the time of hepatocyte harvest permits the readministration of autologous hepatocytes without the need for further surgery or anesthesia. Prospective patients often have comorbid illnesses that predispose them to increased perioperative morbidity. The ability to reinfuse cells without the extra stress brought about by a second laparotomy or other invasive procedure is a significant advantage. The patients can be studied radiologically immediately prior to hepatocyte reinfusion to ensure that the vessel is open and that hepatopetal flow is present.

In preclinical safety studies experiments were performed in dogs and baboons prior to the institution of a human protocol for the treatment of the metabolic disease, FH. The studies were designed to simulate as closely as possible the surgical and hepatocyte transplant procedures required for proposed human trials. Three baboons underwent partial hepatectomy; hepatocytes were isolated, cultured, and transduced with a retroviral vector called pCMV-βA, which contained the human LDL receptor gene, the β-actin promoter, and the cytomegalovirus (CMV) enhancer. The hepatocytes also were exposed to a replication-defective amphotropic virus containing the *lacZ* gene. Hepatocytes were harvested and reinfused via an indwelling catheter placed into the inferior mesenteric vein. All baboons survived the surgical procedure and were well at 24 to 36 months. No acute portal hypertension, measured by water manometry, or long-term evidence of portal vein thrombosis has been detected angiographically or clinically. Biochemical and hematologic parameters have remained within normal limits.[47]

Possible complications of hepatocyte infusion

Several potential complications must be considered when discussing the safety of liver-directed ex vivo gene therapy. Portal vein thrombosis is the most morbid potential complication of the intraportal administration of autologous hepatocytes. There are no data on the incidence of portal vein thrombosis after the intraportal administration of autologous hepatocytes, but in one study, when crude pancreatic tissue preparations were injected into the portal vein in an attempt to ameliorate the diabetes associated with pancreatic resection, a 4% incidence of portal vein thrombosis was noted.[48] The incidence of portal vein thrombosis following an infusion of autologous hepatocytes should be lower because the cells are autologous rather than allogeneic, and the infusate contains a purified suspension of disaggregated cells rather than tissue fragments. Similar data have been published for the intraportal infusion of highly purified islet cell preparations.[49]

Complete thrombosis with organized clot adherent to the endothelium of the portal vein may preclude subsequent liver transplantation. In addition, portal hypertension with the development of ascites or variceal hemorrhage may cause clinical deterioration in patients with already diminished physiologic reserves. In a patient who may require liver transplantation to correct liver failure from a metabolic disease, the development of infection may cause an urgently needed transplant to be deferred, with a potential negative impact on patient well-being. To minimize the risk of infection, the use of prophylactic antibiotics and performance of the operation in an operating room with standard sterile technique is mandatory. The catheter is left in place for 7 to 10 days and can be inspected daily for early signs of infection. If cellulitis or purulent drainage develops, appropriate cultures are obtained and empiric intravenous antibiotic therapy instituted. If necessary, the catheter can be removed prior to hepatocyte reinfusion. The ability to institute prompt treatment and completely remove the prosthetic device should minimize any adverse impact on the patient.

Other methods for portal vein reinfusion

Another strategy for the infusion of genetically altered hepatocytes into the portal vein is cannulation of the umbilical vein remnant in the falciform ligament. This requires the performance of a small midline laparotomy under local, regional, or general anesthesia. The falciform ligament is dissected and the umbilical vein remnant or suitable collateral vessel is identified. This allows delivery of the cell suspension into the portal circulation. Although no clinical studies using hepatocytes have been performed, injection of highly purified pancreatic islets have been introduced without evidence of portal vein thrombosis.[49] However, several drawbacks reduce the enthusiasm for this approach. The umbilical vein remnant may be completely atretic, and prior upper abdominal surgery is usually associated with surgical division of the falciform ligament. If the patient has cirrhotic or noncirrhotic portal hypertension, hepatofugal flow might result in the shunting of transplanted cells away from the liver. Lastly, the infusion volume may be limited due to the size of the vein remnant.

A number of other forms of hepatocyte delivery are possible. The most direct method would be the infusion of cells using approaches developed by interventional radiologists. There are three possible strategies: hepatic arterial reinfusion via femoral puncture, as is used for the delivery of intra-arterial chemotherapy; percutaneous transhepatic/transsplenic injection into the portal vein; and retrograde injection into the portal vein by transjugular hepatic venous puncture. There are risks shared by all three. Bleeding, either overt or occult, may result. Also, portal venous, hepatic arterial, or other major vascular thrombosis may occur, complicating the future performance of a hepatic transplant. Lastly, the cell reinfusion procedures, as currently practiced, take 10 to 14 hours to perform. In children any of these approaches would require the use of a general anesthetic to minimize squirming and the risk of catheter dislodgment or internal organ injury. The additional physiologic burden of such prolonged sedation or anesthesia in a patient population already at risk for adverse events cannot be overestimated.

Despite the risks and logistical issues associated with these approaches, there are several points of merit in their use. Patients with inborn errors of metabolism do not have a coagulopathy such as that seen in patients with fulminant hepatic failure so that transhepatic percutaneous infusion is relatively free of risks of major hemorrhage. Such an approach would be considered in the case of premature catheter removal or thrombosis prior to cell transplantation. Also, the cells could be directed into a subsegmental branch of the portal vein and cell migration could be further minimized by the placement of coils or gelfoam. The main theoretical advantage of interventional techniques is the possibility of decreasing main portal vein thrombosis to a bare minimum by avoiding diffuse occlusion of sinusoids throughout the portal circulation. Laparoscopic delivery of hepatocytes into the patient is a possible alternative approach but would require a second regional or general anesthetic as well as a second surgical procedure.

Intrasplenic injection of hepatocytes

Another approach to hepatocyte transplantation is intrasplenic injection. Results have been reported in the rat by intrasplenically transplanting hepatitis B surface antigen–producing G7 HBV transgenic rat hepatocytes. By in situ analysis, transgenic cells could be seen in the intrahepatic portal spaces, and at longer times became a part of the periportal hepatic lobule. Over half of the cells originally transplanted into the spleen engrafted permanently into the liver.[50] The ability of intrasplenically transplanted hepatocytes to function in a liver-specific manner has been shown to occur by the maintenance of P450b, P450e, albumin, and α-fetoprotein gene expression.[51]

A Japanese group recently has reported on the feasibility of intrasplenic human hepatocyte transplantation. Ten patients with cirrhosis were treated with splenic pulp injections of allogeneic human hepatocytes. Hepatocytes were isolated by infusing a collagenase solution into the liver parenchyma through large-bore needles with additional side hole placement. The average cell yield and viability were 2.9×10^7 and 79%, respectively.

IN SITU LIVER-DIRECTED GENE THERAPY
Recombinant Retroviruses

Retroviruses have been used to accomplish gene transfer into hepatocytes in vivo, as well, but require major (70%) resection to stimulate hepatic regeneration, which has precluded serious consideration of this approach in human trials. Replication-incompetent retrovirus has been used to infect the liver of fetal rats via the intraperitoneal injection of rats in utero or to infect adult rats via direct injection into the portal vein after partial hepatectomy. The genes transferred were the phosphoenolpyruvate carboxykinase (PEPCK) promoter linked either to the amino 3'-glycosyl phosphotransferase (*neo*) gene or the bovine growth hormone gene.[52] The proviral DNA integrated into the hepatic DNA and the chimeric genes were expressed from the PEPCK promoter for as long as 8 months after infection, but low transfer efficiency was a problem, and in hepatectomized rats 1% to 10% transfer was the best that could be achieved.

In a separate study, helper-free recombinant retrovirus coding for a nuclear targeted β-galactosidase was used as a marker to study the transfer efficiency in rat hepatocytes in vivo. Rather than direct injection into the blood-filled liver, asanguineous perfusion of the portal vein was carried out. To increase the efficiency of gene transfer further, 70% hepatectomy was carried out 24 or 48 hours prior to viral infusion.[53] For at least 3 months after gene transfer up to 5% of hepatocytes expressed nuclear β-galactosidase.

CANDIDATE DISEASES FOR LIVER-DIRECTED GENE THERAPY
Familial Hypercholesterolemia

An important issue in the development of gene therapy for FH

Gene therapy for LDL-receptor abnormalities

relates to the specific somatic cell that is the target for gene transfer. The hepatocyte is the preferred target cell for gene therapy of FH, an autosomal dominant disorder caused by abnormalities in the function or expression of LDL-Rs.[54,55] Patients who inherit one abnormal allele have moderate elevations in plasma LDL and suffer premature coronary artery disease (CAD). The prevalence of heterozygotes in most populations is 1 in 500, and they represent approximately 5% of all patients under 45 years of age who have experienced a myocardial infarction. Patients with two abnormal LDL-R alleles (homozygotes or compound heterozygotes) have severe hypercholesterolemia and life-threatening CAD. In preliminary clinical trials, FH will refer to the more severe clinical syndrome that is associated with two abnormal LDL-R alleles.

The molecular basis of FH lies in the gene that encodes LDL-Rs. Characterization of mutant alleles has revealed a variety of mutations, including deletions, insertions, missense mutations, and nonsense mutations.[54,56] This genotypic heterogeneity leads to variable consequences in the biochemical function of the receptor that are classified in four general groups. Class 1 mutations are associated with no detectable protein and are often caused by gene deletions, class 2 mutations lead to abnormalities in intracellular processing of the protein, class 3 mutations specifically affect binding the ligand LDL, and class 4 mutations encode receptor proteins that fail to cluster in coated pits.

Hepatic LDL-Rs contribute to more than 90% of the high-affinity uptake and degradation of LDL in vivo.[57] A complete deficiency of LDL-R activity in FH leads to a precarious metabolic state in which the catabolism of LDL and its precursor lipoprotein, intermediate-density lipoprotein (IDL), is decreased. Diminished high-affinity uptake of IDL leads to a marked overproduction of LDL which, in the setting of decreased LDL catabolism, results in massive hypercholesterolemia.[58]

The WHHL rabbit has been used as an authentic animal model to develop gene therapies for the homozygous or most severe form of life-threatening FH. The WHHL rabbit has a mutation in its LDL-R gene that renders the receptor completely dysfunctional, leading to accelerated atherosclerosis and premature death.[59] Liver tissue was removed from WHHL rabbits and used to isolate hepatocytes and establish primary cultures. Hepatocytes transduced with a gene encoding LDL-R express levels of functional protein that exceed normal endogenous levels.[60] A functional rabbit LDL-R gene was transduced into a high proportion of hepatocytes, using recombinant retroviruses. Transplantation of genetically corrected cells into the animal from which they were derived was associated with a 30% to 40% decrease in serum cholesterol and detectable recombinant LDL-R for up to 6 months.[61]

Based on the preclinical rabbit and nonhuman primate studies, a clinical protocol was initiated to treat five homozygous FH patients by ex vivo gene therapy. Both children and adults are eligible for this therapy. The first patient is a French Canadian woman FH homozygote with symptomatic CAD who had a rela-

Clinical treatment protocols for FH

tively poor prognosis but who could tolerate a noncardiac surgical procedure with acceptable risk.[62] Four additional patients have been treated and are being evaluated to establish metabolic profiles. The therapy is currently conceived as an adjunct to more traditional therapies, such as plasmapheresis and drugs that will be reinstituted 6 weeks after gene therapy. Eligible patients are admitted to the hospital and subjected to a two-step procedure in which a portion of the liver is removed on day 0 and hepatocytes are isolated and plated in culture. Recombinant retroviruses are used to transduce a normal LDL-R gene into the cultured hepatocytes that are harvested on day 3 and infused into the portal circulation of the patient through an indwelling catheter. The patient is evaluated for engraftment of corrected hepatocytes through a series of metabolic and molecular biologic studies. Three months after gene therapy a small amount of liver tissue is harvested by percutaneous biopsy and analyzed for the presence of recombinant-derived DNA and RNA.

Ornithine-Transcarbamylase Deficiency

Ornithine-transcarbamylase deficiency is one of five documented diseases related to disruption of the urea cycle. This cycle consists of five biochemical reactions and is responsible for the conversion of nitrogenous compounds into urea, as well as the de novo synthesis of arginine. Ornithine-transcarbamylase deficiency is inherited as an X-linked disorder and is characterized by neonatal encephalopathy, hypothermia, apnea, and markedly elevated plasma ammonia levels. The OTC enzyme product is found almost exclusively in the liver, making OTC deficiency a candidate for liver-directed gene therapy. In addition, the liver is the source of deamination of a number of amino acids that serve as sources for ammonium production.

The goal: restoration of OTC production

The human OTC gene has been mapped to the short arm of the X chromosome, 12 cM from the Duchenne muscular dystrophy locus.[63] It is subject to X inactivation in females, and heterogeneous immunocytochemical staining of the liver in heterozygous females has been observed.[64] It is probably X-inactivation that causes the development of clinically significant hyperammonemic episodes in female heterozygotes, suggesting that the partial restoration of OTC-containing cells will correct severe disease to a more mild or even asymptomatic form. The active enzyme functions in the mitochondria, where targeting is accomplished by an OTC precursor leader peptide sequence cleaved in the mitochondrial matrix.[65]

Therapy is relatively nonspecific and involves protein intake restriction and activation of other pathways for the metabolism of waste nitrogen. Supplementation with sodium benzoate and sodium phenylacetate cause the synthesis of hippurate and phenylacetylglutamine, which can serve as alternate sources of excretable nitrogen.[66] Anecdotal reports of liver transplantation for OTC deficiency exist, but so far are performed only for intractable coma. The most useful models for congenital urea cycle disorders have been two murine mutations, the sparse fur (*Spf*) mouse[67] and the abnormal skin and hair (*Spf*[ash]) mouse,[68] both of which are OTC-deficient.[69]

Preliminary Attempts at Genetic Correction of OTC Deficiency

Initial attempts at ameliorating the effects of the *Spf* mutation involved the introduction into fertilized *Spf*[ash] eggs of a construct containing a rat OTC cDNA linked to the SV40 early promoter. Successful expression of the transgene resulted in the development of a transgenic *Spf*[ash] mouse whose appearance was normalized. Transgenic approaches in humans lack ethical justification and are irrelevant to expected clinical applications; other strategies must be employed. Stratford-Perricaudet et al[70] explored the potential of recombinant adenovirus for introducing and expressing the normal OTC gene in *Spf*[ash] mice. Their construct, utilizing rat OTC cDNA under the control of the viral MLP, was injected into newborn *Spf*[ash] mice. In this study liver OTC activity rose to normal levels in four of 15 mice and persisted for 1 to 2 months. These mice also exhibited a decrease in urinary orotic acid excretion. Surprisingly, the MLP-OTC mRNA transcripts persisted for over 1 year.

OTC gene transfer experiments

Grompe et al[71] used a defective recombinant retrovirus to transduce primary hepatocyte cultures derived from either *Spf* or *Spf*[ash] mice. Transduction of primary cultures was highly efficient, with an average proviral copy number of 0.5 to 2 per cell in the population of transduced hepatocytes. Northern analysis and slot blots of total RNA isolated from transduced cells showed normal levels of human OTC mRNA and partial correction of levels of OTC activity. Viability after replating exceeded 90%, indicating that the transduced cells might be useful for transplantation. These investigators subsequently used adenoviral vectors, AdSRαhOTC and AdHCMVsp1LacZ for in vitro and in vivo studies. Administering 100 to 200 plaque-forming units (PFU)/cell they detected β-gal expression in 100% of human and more than 40% of adult *Spf* mouse hepatocytes within 72 hours of infection and for up to 2 weeks in culture.[72] AdSRαhOTC was then used to treat newborn *Spf*/Y mice. A single intrajugular injection of 5×10^7 PFUs was sufficient to increase hepatic OTC activity and decrease urinary orotic acid excretion.[73]

Hepatic Bilirubin UDP Glucuronyl Transferase

Bilirubin is a pigment derived from the reticuloendothelial system degradation of heme proteins, including hemoglobin from senescent erythrocytes and the cytochromes P450. It is a lipophilic molecule in its unconjugated state and can cause neonatal kernicterus in high concentrations. Circulating bilirubin is bound to albumin and is avidly cleared in the liver by an unknown mechanism that appears to be carrier-mediated and liver-specific.[74] Inside the hepatocyte, bilirubin binds to ligandin, a form of glutathione-S-transferase, and subsequently is conjugated to any of a number of polar molecules, usually glucuronic acid. The conjugation reaction is catalyzed by a microsomal enzyme, hepatic bilirubin uridine diphosphoglucuronate (UDP) β-D-glucuronosyltransferase [EC 2.4.1.17]. The conjugated bilirubin pigments are subsequently excreted into the bile.

Crigler-Najjar syndrome type I

A congenital deficiency of hepatic bilirubin UDP β-D-glucuronosyltransferase has been identified as the cause of Crigler-Najjar syndrome type I. Six infants in three related families were first reported in 1952.[75] Five of the six died within the first 15 months of life; the sixth lived until the age of 15 years. Over 70 patients have been reported with Crigler-Najjar syndrome type I, and virtually all have died during the neonatal period. The trait is inherited as an autosomal recessive, occurs in all races, and often is associated with consanguinity.[76] The gene coding for one isoform of this enzyme has been cloned and provides the basis for the consideration of gene therapy.

Conventional therapy is directed at reducing bilirubin levels by nonenzymatic means, usually phototherapy or plasmapheresis. Phototherapy is helpful in the neonatal population but becomes impractical for patients older than 3 years of age, as the skin becomes thicker and more heavily pigmented and there is an increase in body mass relative to surface area. Plasmapheresis works by removing albumin, and circulating bilirubin bound to albumin, from the plasma, and is the most effective means of acutely decreasing bilirubin levels. Liver transplantation also has been reported for Crigler-Najjar syndrome type I.[77]

Another important factor in considering Crigler-Najjar syndrome type I for gene therapy is the availability of an animal model for this disease, the Gunn rat. Gunn rats are a mutant Wistar strain with nonhemolytic unconjugated hyperbilirubinemia. Heterozygotes are clinically normal, but homozygotes have unconjugated bilirubin at levels between 3 and 20 mg/dL, pale bile, and frequently develop kernicterus; hence, they are a good experimental model for gene therapy for Crigler-Najjar syndrome type I. Biochemically, five isoforms of UDP glucuronosyltransferase have been identified, two of which are responsible for bilirubin conjugation. Only the type 2 isoform has been cloned; it is believed to be the less active form in vivo.[78]

α₁-ANTITRYPSIN DEFICIENCY

α_1-Antitrypsin (α_1-AT) is a plasma protease inhibitor of 52 kD, and has elastase as its major physiologic substrate. Synthesis, posttranslational modification, and secretion occur primarily in the hepatocyte. PI *Z is the most common disease-causing allele and is inherited in an autosomal recessive manner. PI ZZ homozygotes have only 15% to 20% of the normal plasma levels of α_1-AT. The PI ZZ α_1-AT mutation leads to a single lysine for glutamic acid substitution at position 342 disrupting a salt bridge and altering the three-dimensional structure of the protein. Defects in normal α_1-AT expression and processing, brought about as a result of mutation, can lead to pathology in the lung and liver. Diminished

Manifestations of α_1-AT deficiency

levels of α_1-AT in the blood results in an imbalance between protease/protease inhibitors, allowing the destruction of lung parenchyma. Chronic obstructive pulmonary disease is the most common clinical manifestation of α_1-AT deficiency, with basal lung parenchyma most severely affected.

The liver is the primary site of α_1-AT biosynthesis. In some cases, alteration in the protein sequence of α_1-AT prevents normal posttranslational processing and results in the intracellular accumulation of large quantities of abnormal protein, detectable as intracytoplasmic inclusions.[79] One pathologic consequence of this is the development of liver injury. In one series of patients with homozygous α_1-AT deficiency, 5.2% of patients had cirrhosis, and the incidence increased to 15% in men over the age of 51 years.[80,81]

The introduction of a normal copy of the α_1-AT gene into the hepatocyte is not likely to correct the liver disease. However, the secretion of increased levels of normal α_1-AT into the plasma should ameliorate the obstructive lung disease that is the predominant manifestation of the deficiency. Replacement therapy of α_1-AT might decrease the progression of liver disease, with elevated plasma levels exerting negative feedback on hepatic transcription and translation of aberrant alleles.[82] Using similar logic, transduction of a copy of the normal gene into hepatocytes might dilute out translation products of the mutant gene, decreasing hepatocyte damage.

Treatment strategies   Several strategies have been developed for treating the pulmonary manifestations of α_1-AT deficiency.[83] Prevention is obviously a major part of therapy, and patients should be counseled vigorously to cease smoking. Danazol also has been used, but with only modest success. Several approaches have attempted to restore α_1-AT levels to normal, including the infusion of crude human plasma fractions, aerosol inhalation, and bronchoalveolar lavage with synthetic α_1-AT.[84–88] Orthotopic liver transplantation (OLT) is the only form of therapy capable of correcting both the hepatic and pulmonary manifestations of α_1-AT deficiency. At least 39 patients have undergone OLT for α_1-AT deficiency, with a 5-year actuarial survival rate of about 70%.[89]

The administration of exogenous α_1-AT appears to restore to normal anti-neutrophil elastase defenses.[84,85] A number of experimental models utilizing gene transfer to correct this deficiency have been reported. In one, a retroviral vector was used to insert human α_1-AT cDNA into the genome of mouse fibroblasts, resulting in α_1-AT secretion.[90] Recombinant human α_1-AT cDNA has been successfully transferred to human umbilical vein endothelial cells.[91] A canine model of liver-directed ex vivo gene therapy using retrovirally altered autologous hepatocytes also has been reported.[92] A recent study has addressed the efficacy and safety of using adenoviruses to mediate gene transfer and α_1-AT expression in rat liver. Primary rat hepatocyte cultures infected with a recombinant adenovirus containing a human α_1-AT cDNA synthesized and secreted human α_1-AT for 4 weeks with no evidence of toxicity. Intraportal infusion of recombinant adenovirus at levels of approximately 10 PFU/cell resulted in the expression of β-galactosidase as well as the production of α_1-AT without histologic evidence of liver injury.[93]

HEMOPHILIA B

Hemophilia B (Christmas disease) is a chromosome X-linked blood clotting disorder that results when factor IX is deficient or

Ex vivo factor IX gene transfer to hepatocytes

functionally defective. The enzyme is synthesized in the liver, and the existence of animal models for this genetic disease have permitted the development of somatic gene therapy protocols aimed at the transfer of functional copies of the factor IX gene into the liver. An N2-based recombinant retroviral vector, NCMVFIX, was constructed for the efficient transfer and expression of human factor IX cDNA in primary rabbit hepatocytes. In this construct the human CMV immediate early promoter directed the expression of factor IX. Hepatocytes were isolated from 3-week-old New Zealand white rabbits infected with the recombinant virus and analyzed for secretion of active factor IX. The infected rabbit hepatocytes produced human factor IX that was indistinguishable from functional protein derived from human plasma.[94]

In vivo factor IX hepatic gene transfer

A method was also developed for factor IX hepatic gene transfer in vivo by the direct infusion of recombinant retroviral vectors into the portal vasculature. This technique resulted in the persistent expression of exogenous genes. Using the hemophilia B canine model, canine factor IX cDNA was transduced directly into the hepatocytes of affected dogs in vivo. The expression of the recombinant retrovirus was dependent on a two-thirds partial hepatectomy and cannulation of a splenic vein tributary with a subcutaneously placed catheter for infusion of viral supernatant 24, 48, and 72 hours after hepatectomy. The dogs transduced with canine factor IX recombinant retrovirus constitutively expressed canine factor IX for 5 months after the procedure at a concentration high enough to improve the whole blood clotting time and partial thromboplastin time.[95]

Systemic factor IX replacement

Other cell types have been studied for systemic factor IX replacement. Primary skin fibroblasts from hemophilic dogs were transduced by recombinant retrovirus (LNCdF9L) containing a canine factor IX cDNA. High levels of biologically active canine factor IX (1 μg/10^6 cells per 24 hours) were secreted in the medium. The level of factor IX produced increased substantially if the cells were stimulated by basic fibroblast growth factor during infection.[11] Mouse primary myoblasts were infected with replication-defective retroviruses expressing canine factor IX cDNA under the control of a mouse muscle creatine kinase enhancer and human CMV promoter. The infected myoblasts were injected into the hind legs of recipient mice, and levels of secreted factor IX protein were monitored in the plasma. Sustained expression of factor IX protein for over 6 months without any apparent adverse effect on the recipient mice was noted.[96] Lastly, to develop a gene therapy approach for hemophilia B, human factor IX was expressed and characterized in rat capillary endothelial cells. Moloney MLV–derived retrovirus vectors containing human factor IX cDNA linked to heterologous promoters and the neomycin-resistant gene were constructed and employed. Rat capillary endothelial cells and NIH 3T3 cells infected with these viruses were selected with G418 sulfate and tested for expression of factor IX. A construct with the factor IX cDNA under direct control of the retroviral long-terminal repeats gave the highest levels of expression (0.84 and 3.6 μg/10^6 cells per day for capillary endothelial cells and NIH 3T3 cells, respectively), as quantitated by immunoassays as well as clotting activity assays. A single RNA transcript of 4.4 kb predicted by the construct and a recombinant factor IX of 68 kD identical to purified plasma factor IX were found. The recombinant human factor IX produced showed full clotting activity, demonstrating that capillary endothelial cells have an efficient mechanism for posttranslational modification, including γ-carboxylation, essential for biologic activity.[97]

LIVER CANCER

p53 gene strategy

Several approaches to gene therapy for hepatic cancer, primary as well as metastatic, have been proposed and may prove useful in the near future. In contrast to metabolic disease, where reconstitution of a relatively small proportion of hepatocytes may result in amelioration or cure, all malignant cells in a cancer must be killed selectively. Replacing nonfunctional tumor suppressor genes is an attractive strategy, but genes must be introduced into all cells. In addition, in cases such as *p53*, the presence of mutant *p53* alleles act as a dominant negative mutation in the formation of heterodimers and, as such, not only must normal protein be present, but abnormal protein production must be suppressed.[98]

HSV-tk gene strategy

A different strategy, originally used in the treatment of patients with brain tumors, is based on the selective introduction of the herpes simplex thymidine kinase gene into tumor cells.[99] In proliferating cells, addition of the drug ganciclovir leads to the synthesis of toxic nucleotides which then are incorporated into the newly synthesized DNA and result in cell death. This killing is extended to adjacent cells by the bystander effect, a poorly understood phenomenon. A current hypothesis suggests the transfer of toxic nucleotide from cells containing the transduced gene to genetically unmodified cells by tight junctions or other intracellular communications. The differential killing of proliferating cells and the ability to kill tumors with a transduction efficiency of 10% makes this approach feasible in any tumor with a relatively rapid cycling rate, including hepatic metastases.[100]

Recombinant virus carrying nonmammalian prodrug-activating enzymes

Virus-directed enzyme/prodrug therapy (VDEPT) is based on the premise that tumor-associated transcriptional regulatory sequences can be used to express selectively a nonmammalian prodrug-activating enzyme specifically in cancer cells. The strategy is to allow local metabolism of a nontoxic prodrug to a toxic metabolite. One VDEPT approach that may be employed is the targeting of dividing tumor cells with recombinant viruses carrying the varicella zoster virus thymidine kinase (*VZV-tk*) gene. Using the α-fetoprotein or albumin (both liver-specific) transcriptional regulatory sequences to control the expression of *VZV-tk*, hepatoma cells have been killed selectively.[101]

THE PANCREAS
Cystic Fibrosis

Exocrine pancreatic insufficiency is present in most CF patients from birth.[102] Pathology is caused by the obstruction of ducts by abnormally thick, inspissated secretions resulting from a lack of dilatation of the secretory ducts and flattening of the usually cuboidal epithelium. There is a widespread loss of acini, and intraluminal calcifications, as seen with other types of chronic pancreatitis. The islets of Langerhans are preserved until late, but eventually progressive scarring of the gland is associated with the development of diabetes.

Clinically, pancreatic enzyme deficiency results in protein and fat malabsorption. Stools are greasy, bulky, and foul-smelling. Fat loss may be as high as 70%, and is accompanied by deficiency of the fat-soluble vitamins A, D, E, and K. During the first 6 months of life protein malabsorption can be so severe as to lead to hypoproteinemia and anasarca. With increasing age, low growth rates occur from malnutrition as well as the vitamin-deficiency states of xerophthalmia and night blindness (vitamin A deficiency), diminished bone density (vitamin D deficiency), and coagulopathy (vitamin K deficiency). Classic signs of true pancreatitis occur in only 1% of patients, and are probably due to obstruction of the pancreatic duct by pancreatoliths and

Transducing pancreatic lipase genes via recombinant adenoviruses

extravasation of activated enzymes into the peripancreatic tissues.[103] Recently, recombinant adenoviruses have been used to transduce genes encoding for pancreatic lipase as a way of treating pancreatic enzyme deficiency.[26]

Diabetes is another significant concern in CF patients surviving into adolescence. In one study of patients aged 12 years and older, the incidence of abnormal glucose tolerance tests was 57%.[104] The requirement for insulin is probably closer to 8%.[105] One interesting finding is a decrease in the percentage of β-cells in the islets of CF patients from more than 50%, in normal adults, to approximately 25%.[106] This is important in that oral hypoglycemics are not generally useful in CF patients who instead require insulin to prevent the complications of retinopathy and neuropathy. Recently, insulin resistance has also been documented in CF patients with overt diabetes.[107]

Diabetes Types I and II

Type I diabetes, which is thought to be autoimmune in pathogenesis, and type II diabetes, which appears to encompass a variety of metabolic defects, are common diseases and a source of considerable morbidity and premature mortality. Although the administration of insulin has resulted in diminished complications and a substantial prolongation of life, other approaches need to be considered.[108] Islet and whole pancreas transplantation have been shown to be viable clinical approaches to rendering diabetic patients euglycemic.

Initial work demonstrated that, in the rat, islets could be isolated and transplanted as isografts. Islet isografts have been shown to reverse the diabetic state to normal.[109,110] Transplantation into some sites, such as the liver (via intraportal injection) were successful but other sites, such as the subcutaneous tissue or muscle, were not.[111] In addition to rendering diabetic animals euglycemic, islet transplants could prevent or reverse early diabetic complications in rat models.[112]

Gene therapies for immunomodulation in islet cell grafting

A second major advance was the development of procedures for immunomodulation that prevented the rejection of islet allografts and xenografts in rodents without the need for continuous immunosuppression of the recipient. This initial work in rodents provided the stimulus to develop methods for the mass isolation of human islets. A variety of techniques have been used with success but a thorough discussion is beyond the scope of this section. A recent review has nicely summarized the available data.[113] The realization that human diabetes is not easily modeled in large animals led to the early attempt to move into human clinical trials, despite suboptimal isolation techniques and graft survival.

Gene Therapy of β-Cells to Manipulate Islet Graft Survival and Function

Liver- and pancreas-directed gene therapies

Those forms of diabetes caused by defects in the glucose-sensing pathway may be treatable through virus-mediated reconstitution of gene expression. This heterogeneous group of disorders has been difficult to treat using conventional approaches, often leading to a chronic disabling condition associated with premature mortality. Individually, these inborn errors of metabolism are rare but collectively they contribute significantly to the morbidity and mortality in pediatric patients. Critical to the development and wide application of gene therapies for diabetes is the demonstration in humans that liver-directed gene transfer can lead to efficient and stable genetic reconstitution.[62] The strategy and a technology for the clinical applications of pancreas-directed gene therapy could have equally broad application. The only definitive therapy of diabetes is strict correction of the blood sugar by insulin.[108] The success of pancreatic islet transplantation in correcting the underlying metabolic defect in diabetes suggests that selective reconstitution of pancreatic gene expression by somatic gene transfer should be sufficient for metabolic improvement and clinical efficacy. Although in its infancy, gene therapy to correct diabetes has a promising future.

References

1. Collins F, Galas D. *Science* 1993;262:43-46.
2. Fields C, et al. *Nature Genet* 1994;7:345-346.
3. Williams DA, et al. *Nature* 1984;310:476-480.
4. Wilson JM, et al. *Proc Natl Acad Sci USA* 1988;85:3014-3018.
5. Rosenfeld MA, et al. *Cell* 1992;68:143-155.
6. Muro-Cacho CA, et al. *J Immunother* 1992;11:231-237.
7. Culver K, et al. *Proc Natl Acad Sci USA* 1991;88:3155-3159.
8. Wilson JM, et al. *Science* 1989;244:1344-1346.
9. Wolff JA, et al. *Science* 1990;247:1465-1468.
10. Lin H, et al. *Circulation* 1990;82:2217-2221.
11. Axelrod JH, et al. *Proc Natl Acad Sci USA* 1990;87:5173-5177.
12. Roessler BJ, et al. *J Clin Invest* 1993;92:1085-1092.
13. Palella TD, et al. *Gene* 1989;80:137-144.
14. Cepko CL, et al. *Cell* 1984;37:1053-1062.
15. Ghosh-Choudhury G, Graham FL. *Biochem Biophys Res Commun* 1987;147:964-973.
16. Rosenfeld MA, et al. *Science* 1991;252:431-434.
17. Samulski RJ, et al. *J Virol* 1989;63:3822-3828.
18. Felgner PL, et al. *Proc Natl Acad Sci USA* 1987;84:7413-7417.
19. Nicolau C, et al. *Methods Enzymol* 1987;149:157-176.
20. Wu GY, Wu CH. *J Biol Chem* 1988;262:4429-4432, 263:588.

21. Varmus H, Swanstrom R, in Weiss R, et al (eds). *RNA Tumor Viruses.*
    New York, NY, Cold Spring Harbor Press, 1984, pp 369-512.
22. Mulligan RC, in Lindsten J, Pettersson U (eds). *Etiology of Human
    Disease at the DNA Level.* New York, NY, Raven Press, 1991,
    pp 143-189.
23. Miller DG, et al. *Molec Cell Biol* 1990;10:4239-4242.
24. Miller AD. *Hum Gene Ther* 1990;1:5-14.
25. Roe TY, et al. *EMBO J* 1993;12:2099-2108.
26. Crystal RG, et al. *Nat Genet* 1994;8:42-50.
27. Yang YY, et al. *Proc Natl Acad Sci USA* 1993;90:4601-4605.
28. Shenk T, Williams J. *Curr Topics Microbiol Immunol* 1984;111:1-38.
29. Horwitz MS, in Fields BN, et al (eds). *Virology.* New York, NY, Raven
    Press, 1990, pp 1679-1721.
30. Graham FL, et al. *J Gen Virol* 1977;36:59-72.
31. Kozarsky KF, Wilson JM. *Curr Opinion Genet Devel* 1993;3:499-503.
32. Yang Y, et al. *Proc Natl Acad Sci USA* 1993;91:4407-4411.
33. Yang Y, et al. *Nature Genet* 1994;7:362-369.
34. Srivastava A, et al. *J Virol* 1983;45:555-564.
35. Muzyczka N. *Curr Topics Microimmunol* 1992;158:97-129.
36. Samulski RJ, et al. *EMBO J* 1991;10:3941-3950.
37. Walsh CE, et al. *Proc Natl Acad Sci USA* 1992;89:7257-7261.
38. Wondisford FE, et al. *Mol Endocrinol* 1988;2:32-39.
39. Smith JG, et al. *Biochem Biophys Acta* 1993;1154:327-340.
40. Wu GY, et al. *J Biol Chem* 1991;266:14338-14342.
41. Horwitz AL. *Curr Topics Microbiol Immunol* 1991;168:185-200.
42. Bilheimer DW, et al. *N Engl J Med* 1994;311:1658-1664.
43. Moscioni AD, et al. *Gastroenterology* 1989;96:1546-1551.
44. Farney AC, Sutherland DER, in Ricordi C (ed). *Pancreatic Islet Cell
    Transplantation.* Austin, Tex, RG Landes, 1992, pp 291-312.
45. Grossman M, et al. *Som Cell Mol Genet* 1991;17:601-607.
46. Raper SE, et al. *Surgery* 1992;112:333-340.
47. Grossman M, et al. *Hum Gene Ther* 1992;3:501-510.
48. Memsic L, et al. *Surgery* 1984;95:238-242.
49. Scharp DW, et al. *Transplantation* 1991;51:76-85.
50. Gupta S, et al. *Hepatology* 1991;14:144-149.
51. Maganto P, et al. *Hepatology* 1990;11:585-592.
52. Hatzoglou M, et al. *J Biol Chem* 1990;265:17285-17293.
53. Ferry N, et al. *Proc Natl Acad Sci USA* 1991;88:8377-8381.
54. Goldstein JL, Brown MS, in Scriver CR, et al (eds). *Metabolic Basis of
    Inherited Disease,* ed 6. New York, NY, McGraw-Hill, 1989,
    pp 1215-1250.
55. Brown MS, Goldstein JL. *Science* 1986;232:34-47.
56. Russell DW, et al. *Arteriosclerosis* 1989;9(suppl I):I8-I13.
57. Turley SD, Dietschy JM, in Arias IM, et al (eds). *The Liver: Biology and
    Pathophysiology,* ed 2. New York, NY, Raven Press, 1988, pp 617-641.
58. Goldstein JL, et al. *N Engl J Med* 1983;309:288-296.
59. Watanabe Y. *Atherosclerosis* 1980;36:261-268.
60. Wilson JM, et al. *Proc Natl Acad Sci USA* 1988;85:4421-4425.
61. Roy-Choudhury J, et al. *Science* 1991;254:1802-1805.
62. Grossman M, et al. *Nature Genet* 1994;6:335-341.
63. Lindgren V, et al. *Science* 1984;226:698-700.
64. Ricciuti FC, et al. *Am J Hum Genet* 1976;28:332-338.
65. Mori M, et al. *Mol Cell Biochem* 1982;49:97-111.
66. Brusilow SW, Horwich AL, in Scriver CR, et al (eds). *Metabolic Basis of
    Inherited Disease,* ed 6. New York, NY, McGraw-Hill, 1989, pp 629-663.
67. DeMars R, et al. *Proc Natl Acad Sci USA* 1976;73:1693-1697.
68. Doolittle DP, et al. *J Hered* 1974;65:194-195.
69. Spector EB, Mazzochi RA. *Prog Clin Biol Res* 1983;127:85-96.
70. Stratford-Perricaudet LD, et al. *Hum Gene Ther* 1990;1:241-256.
71. Grompe M, et al. *Hum Gene Ther* 1992;3:35-44.
72. Morsy MA, et al. *J Clin Invest* 1993;92:1580-1586.
73. Morsy MA, et al. *Am J Hum Genet* 1993;53(suppl 3):217A.

74. Scharschmidt BF, et al. *J Clin Invest* 1975;56:1280-1292.
75. Crigler JF, Najjar VA. *Pediatrics* 1952;10:169-180.
76. Roy-Choudhury J, in Scriver CR, et al (eds). *Metabolic Basis of Inherited Disease*, ed 6. New York, NY, McGraw-Hill, 1989, pp 1367-1408.
77. Kaufman SS, et al. *Hepatology* 1986;6:1259-1262.
78. Bosma PJ, et al. *Hepatology* 1992;16(suppl _):79A.
79. Bathurst IC, et al. *FEBS Letter* 1984;177:179-183.
80. Cox DW, Smyth S. *Am J Med* 1983;74:221-227.
81. Eriksson S, et al. *N Engl J Med* 1986;314:736-739.
82. Birrer P, et al. *J Inherit Metab Dis* 1991;14:512-525.
83. Janoff A. *Am Rev Respir Dis* 1985;132:417-433.
84. Hubbard RC, et al. *Ann Intern Med* 1989;111:206-212.
85. McElvaney NG, et al. *Lancet* 1991;337:392-394.
86. Gadek JE, et al. *J Clin Invest* 1981;68:1158-1165.
87. Straus SD, et al. *Biochem Biophys Res Comm* 1985;130:1177-1184.
88. Wewers MD, et al. *N Engl J Med* 1987;316:1055-1062.
89. Esquivel CO, et al. *Transplant Proc* 1987;19:3798-3802.
90. Garver RI, et al. *Science* 1987;237:762-764.
91. Lemarchand P, et al. *Proc Natl Acad Sci USA* 1992;89:6482-6486.
92. Kay MA, et al. *Proc Natl Acad Sci USA* 1992;89:89-93.
93. Jaffe HA, et al. *Nature Genet* 1992;1:372-378.
94. Armentano D, et al. *Proc Natl Acad Sci USA* 1990;87:6141-6145.
95. Kay MA, et al. *Science* 1993;262:117-119.
96. Dai Y, et al. *Proc Natl Acad Sci USA* 1992;89:10892-10895.
97. Yao SN, et al. *Proc Natl Acad Sci USA* 1991;88:8101-8105.
98. Kern SE, et al. *Science* 1992;256:827-830.
99. Culver KW, et al. *Science* 1992;256:1550-1552.
100. Caruso M, et al. *Proc Natl Acad Sci USA* 1993;90:7024-7028.
101. Huber BE, et al. *Proc Natl Acad Sci USA* 1991;88:8039-8043.
102. DiSant'agnese PA, Hubbard VS, in Taussig LM (ed). *Cystic Fibrosis*. New York, NY, Thieme-Stratton, 1984, p 230.
103. Shwachman H, et al. *Pediatrics* 1975;55:86-95.
104. Rodman HM, Matthews LW, in Warwick WJ (ed). *100 Years of Cystic Fibrosis*. Minneapolis, Minn, University of Minnesota Press, 1981, p 67.
105. DiSant'agnese PA, Davis PB. *Am J Med* 1979;66:121-132.
106. Abdul-Karim FW, et al. *Arch Pathol Lab Med* 1986;110:602-606.
107. Moran A, et al. *Diabetes* 1994;43:1020-1026.
108. DCCT Research Group. *N Engl J Med* 1993;329:977-986.
109. Lacy PE, Kostianovsky M. *Diabetes* 1967;16:35-39.
110. Reckard CR, Barker CF. *Transplant Proc* 1973;5:761-763.
111. Kemp CB, et al. *Diabetologia* 1973;9:486-491.
112. Mauer S, et al. *Diabetes* 1974;23:748-753.
113. Lacy PE. *Diabetes Rev* 1993;1:76-92.

II Gene Therapy for Vascular Disease

Louis M. Messina, MD
Theodore H. Welling III, BS
Rajabrata Sarkar, MD
Charles J. Shanley, MD
James C. Stanley, MD

INTRODUCTION

Gene therapy involves the transfer of recombinant genes into specific target cells in a patient to treat human disease. In *cell-mediated gene therapy* specific target cells are harvested from the patient, transduced ex vivo, and transplanted back into the patient. In *direct gene transfer* the transgene is transferred into the target cells in vivo. In this way one can replace a defective or missing gene for a genetic disease or suppress abnormal gene function in an acquired disease.

Somatic gene therapy in vascular diseases

Vascular diseases are excellent candidates for somatic gene therapy, as most are focal processes characterized by vascular cell proliferation and increased matrix deposition in diseased arteries. Vascular cells can be modified genetically to inhibit intimal hyperplasia or modulate the inflammatory response to vessel wall injury. They also can be transduced to enhance their fibrinolytic activity and thereby decrease the thrombogenicity of a diseased vessel or synthetic vascular graft. The principal target cells used in gene therapy of vascular disease are endothelial cells and vascular smooth muscle cells.

Endothelial cells targeted

Endothelial cells have played an important role in the development of somatic gene therapy for vascular disease. They regulate blood coagulation and fibrinolysis, vasomotor tone, solute and protein exchange between blood and tissues, angiogenesis, and systemic immune and inflammatory responses.[1-4] They are durable cells whose half-lives are measured in years. Additionally, they are pluripotent, whereby their phenotypic expression is regulated by their local environment. This enhances their capacity for successful transplantation to different locations within the circulatory system. Finally, and most importantly, endothelial cells are located at the blood-tissue interface. These characteristics provide a unique mechanism by which to achieve the various autocrine, paracrine, and endocrine effects of recombinant proteins. For these reasons endothelial cells have received considerable attention as target cells for gene therapy.[5-9]

Vascular smooth muscle cells targeted

Recently, vascular smooth muscle cells have also become important target cells for the purpose of gene therapy. They are largely responsible for the structure and function of the vascular wall, of which they comprise the largest cell population. As such, they are an obvious target for somatic gene therapy. The unregulated growth of vascular smooth muscle contributes to the progression of atherosclerosis and intimal hyperplasia. This section reviews the experimental work undertaken in the use of vascular cells for gene therapy for vascular diseases.

GENE TRANSFER TO VASCULAR CELLS IN VITRO
Overview of Gene Transfer Techniques

Table 1

Transgenes may be introduced into cells by a variety of methods (Table 1), principally via DNA plasmids and replication-incompetent viral vectors that contain the transgene of interest.[10,11] A critical factor in durable gene therapy is the incorporation of the transgene into the chromosomal DNA of the host target cell. It is usually only under this condition that expression of the transgene persists after host cell proliferation. At this time,

Table 1. Methods of Gene Transfer to Vascular Cells
Chemical Calcium phosphate coprecipitation Cationic liposome Hemagglutinating virus of Japan–Liposome complex
Physical Microinjection Pneumatic injection DNA-coated gold particles Electroporation
Viral Vectors Retrovirus Adenovirus Adeno-associated virus Herpes simplex

retroviral or adeno-associated viral vectors must be used to ensure this transgene persistence.

Gene transfer by plasmids has been accomplished under a variety of experimental conditions. Cells in culture exposed to a plasmid will take up the plasmid, but only at a low rate of efficiency.[12] These simple plasmid constructs consist of the transgene, a promoter, and a polyadenylation signal that are incorporated into a bacterial plasmid backbone (Fig. 1). Chemical techniques to enhance plasmid-DNA transfer include the use of calcium phosphate coprecipitation, receptor-mediated transfer in which the DNA is complexed to a polypeptide targeted to a receptor on the target cell surface, and lipofection,[13,14] which is accomplished by encapsulation of the DNA within polycationic liposomes.[15]

Figure 1

Physical techniques also have been used to transfer DNA to target cells. Those most commonly employed are microinjection of the DNA and electroporation, whereby a high-voltage electric

Plasmid Vector

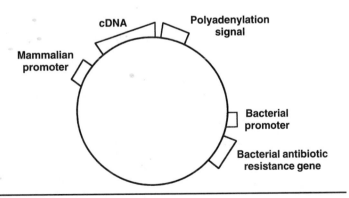

Fig. 1. Schematic illustration of an expression of plasmid vector.

shock induces the formation of pores in the cell membrane, which promotes the transfer of DNA into the cell.[16] These chemical and physical techniques are safe and do not necessarily limit the size of the transgene used for transfer.

Liposome-mediated
gene transfer

Liposome-DNA complexes were developed to avoid the potential complications of using viral vectors to deliver a transgene into a target cell.[15] Fusion between the liposome-DNA complex and the cell membrane can lead to gene transfer into the cytoplasm without lysozyme degradation. Cationic liposomes are composed of a positively charged lipid, such as N-[1-(2, 3-dioleyloxy)propyl]-N,N,N-trimethylammonium (DOTMA) that, when mixed with an equal concentration of the neutral lipid dioleoyl phosphotidylethanolamine (DOPE), forms liposomes that complex with DNA or RNA. These complexes have a net positive charge that facilitates their interaction with the negatively charged cell surface as well as the negatively charged nucleic acid. After entering the cytoplasm, the plasmid moves to the nucleus where it persists for a limited time as an extrachromosomal element, an *episome*. Integration into the host chromosome can occur, but only at very low frequencies.

Replication-incompetent
viral vectors

Many replication-incompetent viral vectors have been developed to facilitate gene transfer to target cells.[17-23] These viral vectors are propagated in packaging cell lines that have been transfected with the viral genes necessary for synthesis of an infectious but replication-incompetent viral vector.[17]

Retroviruses are small, 10-kb RNA viruses whose two identical copies of the single-stranded RNA genome are converted into DNA within an infected cell by the enzyme *reverse transcriptase*.[17-19] In addition to this enzyme, the virus particle contains the enzymes *integrase*, which promotes integration of the proviral DNA into the host genome, and *protease*, which cleaves the *gag-pol* polyproteins into other proteins, such as integrase or reverse-transcriptase. Retroviruses bind to cells in a receptor-mediated fashion by cell surface proteins that recognize viral envelope proteins. After infecting a cell, opening of the viron occurs and a nucleoprotein complex forms in which viral RNA is copied under the influence of its enzyme reverse transcriptase into DNA. This nucleoprotein complex translocates to the nucleus and integrates into the host's chromosomes.

This capacity to achieve stable incorporation of a transgene into a host cell's chromosomes is the principal advantage of retroviral vectors. However, they can incorporate only a relatively short length of transgene RNA, and retroviruses can incorporate successfully only in host cells that are actively dividing, which limits the target cell pool. Potential complications of retroviral vector-mediated gene transfer include the generation of replication-competent viruses during virus assembly in the packaging cell and insertional mutagenesis, which occurs when the virus inserts near and activates a proto-oncogene, causing a malignant transformation of the cell.[24]

Adenoviruses are large, 36-kb double-stranded DNA viruses capable of infecting a wide range of mammalian cells.[20-23] The adenovirus serotypes Ad 2 and Ad 5 can cause respiratory disease in humans and are being developed for a wide variety of uses in gene therapy. Neither has been associated with human malignancy.[25] In fact, live adenoviruses have been used extensively as vaccines in humans.

The adenovirus is an icosahedral, nonenveloped virus whose genetics and virology have been well-characterized. The 36-kb DNA is divided into 100 map units, each of which is 360 base pairs in length. The DNA contains short inverted terminal repeats, one at each end of the genome, that are required for viral DNA replication. The gene products are organized into early (E1 through E4) and late (L1 through L5) regions, based on expression before or after initiation of viral DNA synthesis during the virus infection cycle.

Adenoviruses are thought to infect cells via receptor-mediated endocytosis into the cells' lysosomal compartments. The viral DNA escapes degradation by lysosomal enzymes due to the presence of terminal proteins linked covalently to the ends of the viral genome. The viron then translocates to the nucleus. The viral DNA retains its linear structure and rarely integrates into the chromosome of the host cell. Subsequently, the transcription of early genes (E1a) induces DNA replication while the expression of late genes mediates virus particle assembly and subsequent lysis of the host cell. These effects of E1 would be undesirable for *Replication-incompetent* gene therapy. Therefore, replication-defective adenoviral vectors *adenoviral vectors* are constructed by replacing the E1a region of the E1 gene with the gene utilized for gene therapy. Like the retroviruses, the replication-defective adenoviruses are produced in a permissive cell line (human embryonic kidney 293 cells) that contains in its genome an integrated copy of the adenovirus E1 region. By homologous recombination between the integrated E1 region and the region containing the transgene, replication-defective but infectious viral particles can be produced in a very high titer, often greater than 10^{11} plaque-forming units (PFU)/mL. The *Advantages* availability of these very high titers is particularly advantageous for in vivo gene therapy. In addition, the capacity of the adenovirus to infect nondividing cells makes adenovirus-mediated gene transfer the best means of achieving high transduction efficiency.

Disadvantages The primary disadvantages of adenoviral vectors is their transient expression. In addition, there are concerns about the safety of direct adenoviral gene transfer. The inhalation of Ad 5 has been associated with interstitial pneumonitis in the rodent, and lymphocytic infiltration has been observed in murine livers following the intravenous injection of the virus.[26,27] Recent evidence suggests that cells transfected with adenoviral vectors induce an immune response that also limits the duration of their transgene expression.[28]

Gene Transfer by Retroviral Vectors

Retroviral gene transfer The earliest reports of gene transfer to endothelial cells eluci-
into endothelial cells dated the mechanisms that regulate endothelial cell–specific gene expression.[29–32] In 1989 Zweibel et al published the first report of the retroviral-mediated transduction of human endothelial cells for the purpose of gene therapy.[33,34] They employed

three retroviral vectors expressing three transgenes. One transgene was neomycin phosphotransferase, which is employed frequently in the construction of viral and nonviral plasmid vectors and allows cells to grow in the presence of the neomycin analogue G418. This analogue is cytocidal to cells without this transgene. Therefore, even if the transduction rate is only 2% to 5%, growth of the cells in G418 will permit selection of a nearly pure population of transduced cells due to the death of the nontransduced cells. These investigators also created retroviral vectors containing the transgene for human adenosine deaminase (ADA) and rat growth hormone as examples of nonsecreted and secreted proteins, respectively. By incorporating neomycin resistance into these retroviral vectors, relatively pure populations of transduced cells could be isolated despite a rather low transfection efficiency.

To evaluate the potential of these transduced cells for vascular gene therapy, the investigators grew the cells onto the surfaces of synthetic vascular grafts where they remained viable for 32 days. In addition, these cells continued to secrete rat growth hormone. These experiments established the feasibility of using retroviral vectors for gene transfer into endothelial cells.

Feasibility studies

Wilson et al also showed that transduced endothelial cells could achieve stable expression of the low density–lipoprotein receptor and secrete human parathyroid hormone.[35] The latter is of note because parathyroid hormone requires extensive post-translational peptide modification to achieve functional activity. Initial transfection efficiencies varied widely in this study, from 5% to 60%.

Increasing endothelial cell expression of the tPA gene

One of the most important genes under consideration for gene therapy of vascular cells is the gene for human tissue plasminogen activator (tPA). The augmented secretion of tPA by human endothelial cells in vivo could be used to reduce the incidence of acute thrombosis following percutaneous transluminal angioplasty of coronary or peripheral arterial atherosclerotic stenoses. The thrombogenicity of small-caliber, synthetic vascular grafts could be reduced by seeding autologous tPA-transduced endothelial cells. Considerable work has been done by a number of investigators to determine the feasibility and consequences of augmenting the expression of the human tPA gene in endothelial cells.[32-36]

Dichek et al have undertaken a series of elegant studies with the goal of enhancing the fibrinolytic activity of endothelial cells by retroviral vector-mediated gene transfer and expression of the human tPA gene in sheep endothelial cells.[36-40] They constructed a retroviral vector with the cDNA for human tPA, driven by an SV40 early promoter. Underlying these experiments were the assumptions that the exquisitely controlled balance between intravascular coagulation and fibrinolysis is mediated largely by endothelial cells, the fibrinolytic activity of the circulating blood is dependent on the circulating concentration of active tPA, and the secretion of tPA by human endothelial cells is dependent on the intracellular concentration of tPA mRNA.[36]

In the first experiment a retroviral vector construct was used to transduce sheep arterial endothelial cells, resulting in a 30-fold increase in tPA secretion over that of control endothelial cells. This increase averaged 100 ng/24 h, was durable, and lasted for at least 11 weeks. In contrast, secretion by transduced venous endothelium was not stable, declining by 50% within 6 weeks. A critical finding was that the secreted tPA was functionally active but the fibrinolytic activity relative to the concentration of protein secreted was less than anticipated. To explain this, these investigators used casein zymography, an in situ enzymatic assay of the different protein moieties separated by gel electrophoresis, to document that much of the recombinant tPA was not free but rather bound by plasminogen activator inhibitor–1 (PAI-1). In spite of this finding, it is noteworthy that the tPA secretion rate was higher than any reported previously by endothelium. Although much of the recombinant tPA was bound, the total activity of endogenous sheep plasminogen activators was increased. Thus, it was established that retroviral-mediated tPA gene transfer causes a net increase in endothelial cell fibrinolytic activity.

Human endothelial cells transfected with the tPA gene

Dichek et al then transduced human umbilical vein endothelial cells with this same B2NSt retroviral vector to determine whether human endothelium could be transduced by such a vector to achieve similar results.[36] Northern blot analysis for the tPA RNA showed the appropriate transcript to be present only in the transduced endothelial cells. The amount of the transcript generated was approximately 100% to 200% of the endogenous tPA transcript level. In addition, the concentration of the tPA antigen in the medium of the transduced cells was two to three times that of control cells.

Optimizing gene transfer

To optimize transfection efficiencies using retroviral vectors expressing β-galactosidase or urokinase genes, the investigators examined a variety of techniques, including extended periods of exposure to the vector, repeated exposure to the vector, maximization of the ratio of the vector particles to endothelial cells, cocultivation of endothelial cells with the vector-producing cells, and variations in the type and concentration of polycation used with the retroviral vector.[38] Only two experimental variables improved the efficiency of gene transfer significantly: the use of a more concentrated, high-titer supernatant and the use of the polycation DEAE-dextran (Pharmacia, Uppsala, Sweden). A 60-second exposure to 1 ng/mL of DEAE-dextran followed by a single 6-hour exposure to the supernatant with a titer of 10^5 to 10^6 colony-forming units (CFU)/mL resulted in transduction efficiencies of 50% to 90%. Reducing the exposure time from 6 hours to 15 minutes resulted in a reduction of transduction efficiency to between 15% and 20%.

Figure 2

Podrazik, in our laboratory, took another approach to optimizing the transduction of human endothelial cells by retroviral vectors, using an MFG retroviral vector containing the human tPA gene (Fig. 2; see page 34).[41] This MFG-tPA vector expressed tPA from a transcript initiated at the 5'-long terminal repeat sequence. A ψ-CRIP producer cell line was used to generate this MFG-tPA vector at titers of 5×10^5 to 1.5×10^6 CFU/mL. In adult canine jugular venous endothelial cells the duration and number

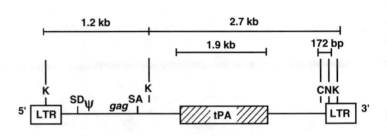

Fig. 2. Schematic representation of the MFG-tPA vector. The backbone of the vector is the murine Moloney leukemia virus including the long-terminal repeat (LTR) and flanking sequences, with the human tPA cDNA. The Kpn I (K restriction site) is depicted as well as the Cla I (C) to Nhe I (Frag). SD, splice donor sequence; ψ, retroviral packaging sequence; *gag*, sequences for viral core protein; SA, splice acceptor sequence; kb, kilobases; bp, base pair. (From Podrazik, et al.[41] Reprinted with permission.)

of retroviral exposures yielding optimal transgene expression was determined for tPA antigen secretion and functional activity in the cell culture medium at 2 and 14 days post transduction. Durable secretion of human tPA by the transduced endothelial cells persisted in all experimental groups and ranged from 6.8 to 53 ng/mL per 10^6 cells per hour. The highest level of antigen secretion and functional activity was identified in the endothelial cells that underwent two 12-hour exposures to the retroviral vector. Between 87% and 95% of cells were positive by immunocytochemical staining (Fig. 3). This highly efficient gene transfer in the absence of selection by neomycin has considerable importance to clinical somatic gene therapy. The selection of

Figure 3

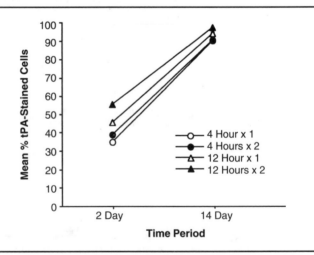

Fig. 3. Difference in immunohistochemical staining of cellular tPA among exposure regimens at 2 and 14 days following the transfection of endothelial cells. At both time points the percentage of exposed cells that stained positive for the tPA antigen increased as the duration of exposure increased. All exposure regimens showed a significantly higher rate of successful transduction at 14 days than at 2 days. (From Podrazik, et al.[41] Reprinted with permission.)

cells in neomycin or its analogue G418 requires an additional 2 to 4 weeks and serial passaging of the cells. This may pose significant risks of injury and bacterial contamination of the cultured endothelial cells.

Question of tPA levels and phenotype expression

A number of concerns have been raised regarding the safety of the very high levels of tPA secreted by these transduced cells. The formation of plasmin, catalyzed by plasminogen activators released from cancer cells, appears to play a role in the degradation of the surrounding extracellular matrix which characterizes the invasive growth of malignant tumors. Plasminogen activators also induce phenotypic changes in these cells that appear to be receptor-mediated.[39] Thus, another important issue raised by these experiments is whether a 30-fold increase in tPA secretion will alter endothelial cell phenotype.

To examine the effects of substantial increases in tPA antigen secretion and fibrinolytic activity on endothelial cell morphology, adhesion, proliferation, migration, and invasion, Jaklitsh et al studied endothelial cells transduced with the B2NSt vector and a control vector, as well as nontransduced endothelial cells.[39] Importantly, retroviral B2NSt transduction had a minimal effect on cell function. The morphology of the two transduced cell populations was unchanged. A small decrease in the horizontal migration rate of transduced cells was identified. Additional experiments showed no other significant differences between the transduced and nontransduced endothelial cells. These in vitro studies established that a high concentration of tPA antigen and activity in B2NSt-transduced G418-selected endothelial cells did not appreciably affect their phenotype in vitro. These results are consistent with those of others that increases in tPA in the areas of malignant transformed cells are relevant but probably not sufficient to account for the phenotypic changes observed in malignant cells.

Question of tPA levels and functional effects

Another concern regarding the use of tPA-transduced cells is their capacity to exert a functional effect in vivo. Any potential increase in fibrinolytic activity secondary to the secretion of recombinant tPA into the large circulating blood volume may be negated by dilution. Another question is whether the increased secretion of recombinant tPA is accompanied by a concomitant increase in PAI-1, which would lead to the subsequent binding and inactivation of the recombinant tPA. Lee et al undertook a series of experiments to study the likelihood of tPA-transduced endothelial cells exerting an important functional effect in vivo.[40] They utilized a novel strategy involving the creation of a mutant single-chain urokinase PA (scu-PA) bound to the apical cell membrane surface. Single-chain urokinase plasminogen activator is a proenzyme that resists binding by PAI-1. It is secreted by human endothelial cells and circulates in the plasma at concentrations of 5 to 10 ng/mL. The recombinant scu-PA has a proenzyme resistant to PAI-1 inhibition anchored to the apical surface of the endothelial cell. In these studies, scu-PA was expressed on the apical surface of the transduced endothelial cells at a concentration of 10^6 molecules per cell, and was converted by plasmin to a double-chain urokinase. The investigators showed that scu-PA anchored to the endothelial cell surface resulted in significantly increased PA functional activity. Such a modification of gene expression by endothelium could play a significant role in the management of intravascular thrombosis and the reduction of thrombogenicity of small-caliber synthetic grafts.

Many investigators are interested in the augmentation of tPA secretion by gene transfer to enhance the fibrinolytic activity of endothelial cells as a technique to manage thrombotic disease in humans. An alternative strategy for reducing the thrombogenicity of blood vessels and synthetic grafts is reducing platelet adhesion and aggregation by augmenting prostacyclin (PGI_2) secretion by the endothelium.[42] The extent of PGI_2 synthesis is determined by the concentration of prostaglandin H synthase (PGHS-1), which reflects the balance between PGHS-1 de novo synthesis and autoinactivation during catalysis.

Reducing platelet adhesion by augmenting PGI_2 secretion

To explore the use of gene transfer to enhance prostacyclin secretion by endothelial cells, Xu et al used a retroviral vector called BAG (β-galactosidase after *gag*) containing the cDNA of human PGHS-1 to augment the expression of prostacyclin H synthase. In their initial studies using a BAG vector containing the PGHS-1 cDNA in the sense orientation, there was a 30-fold increase in mRNA but no increase in PGHS protein or PGI_2. This was apparently due to a frame shift causing inaccurate transcription and translation. However, when the PGHS-1 cDNA was placed in reverse orientation relative to the viral promoter, substantial increases in PGHS mRNA, protein, enzymatic activity, and PGI_2 were noted.

Gene transfer studies of atherosclerosis

Several studies of gene transfer to vascular cells in vitro have established the feasibility of these applications to endothelium, including a study in which gene transfer was used to help explain the mechanism of atherosclerosis. One hypothesis regarding the pathogenesis of atherosclerosis is that arterial wall injury is followed by the migration of circulating monocytes into the arterial wall where they differentiate into macrophages, accumulate lipids and, subsequently, develop into foam cells. Human macrophage colony-stimulating factor (M-CSF) has been shown to direct the terminal differentiation and survival of macrophages. Ramos et al recently cloned the human M-CSF gene into a retroviral vector and transduced rabbit endothelial and smooth muscle cells.[43] DNA polymerase chain reaction (PCR) confirmed that copies of M-CSF gene were present in the transduced cells. Western blot analysis of the conditioned media showed secretion of the intact recombinant protein reaching concentrations of 2 to 8 mg/mL. Functional activity was confirmed by the stimulation of mouse bone marrow cell proliferation. These transduced cells could be utilized in an in vitro model to study the mechanisms regulating the development of atherosclerotic plaque.

A second application of retroviral-mediated gene transfer to endothelium has been proposed for the management of hemophilia B, a recessive disorder caused by a defective factor IX gene. This gene has been mapped to the X-chromosome. Restoration of factor IX levels to 15% of normal can convert a patient with severe bleeding manifestations to one with only mild

Factor IX gene therapy

bleeding episodes. Restoration of factor IX levels to 30% of normal results in the near-complete elimination of the clinical complications of hemophilia B. Yao et al constructed a retroviral vector that contained the human factor IX cDNA linked to a promoter and the neomycin resistance gene.[44] Following transduction and selection of endothelial cells, high levels of transgene expression were documented. Transduced cells secreted active human factor IX at a concentration of 3.6 mg/10^6 cells per 24 hours. The investigators showed that rat capillary endothelial cells were able to complete the extensive posttranslational modification of this protein that is necessary for it to achieve full clotting activity. These results establish the potential application of endothelial cells in the management of noncardiovascular diseases by gene therapy.

Gene Transfer by Adenoviral Vectors In Vitro

Adenoviral vectors are capable of highly efficient gene transfer to a variety of tissues, including liver, lung, skeletal muscle, and blood vessels.[45] Their central role in somatic gene therapy is a result of their availability in high titers, their capacity to infect a wide variety of species and tissues, and their ability to infect and achieve transgene expression in nondividing cells. Their major disadvantages are the short duration of transgene expression due to their inability to incorporate into the host cell chromosomal DNA and the capacity of adenovirus-transduced cells to initiate an immune response due to viral proteins expressed after target cell infection.[28]

Feasibility studies

Lemarchand et al were the first to evaluate the feasibility of using replication-deficient recombinant adenovirus to transfer human genes into human endothelium.[46] They infected human umbilical vein endothelial cells in vitro with adenoviral vectors containing the *lacZ* gene or the human α_1-antitrypsin (α_1-AT) cDNA. The α_1-AT cDNA was chosen because it directs the synthesis of a protein that is not normally secreted by endothelial cells and that requires additional posttranslational modification. Within 6 hours of transduction the endothelial cells expressed human α_1-AT transcripts, as evinced by in situ hybridization and Northern blot analysis. Functional α_1-AT was detected de novo in its active glycosylated form. In addition, expression of this transgene was durable for at least 18 days, and the transduced cells secreted functionally active protein at the rate of 0.3 to 0.6 mg/10^6 cells per 24 hours. To determine the transduction efficiency of this vector, endothelial cells were exposed in vitro to the adenoviral vector containing the *lacZ* cDNA driven by a Rous sarcoma virus (RSV) promoter. The investigators documented highly efficient gene transfer, with an average of 88% of the cells being transduced.

These same investigators also studied the feasibility of using these adenoviral vectors for gene transfer to human endothelial cells under in vitro conditions in which the vessel wall architecture remains intact.[46] Uninfected umbilical veins and veins exposed to the same adenovirus but containing the cystic fibrosis transmembrane conductance regulator (CFTR) were exposed to

Figure 4

the adenoviral vector containing *lacZ*. Histochemical staining showed extensive transgene expression in the intima of these vessels (Fig. 4). In addition, microscopic examination showed that the normal architecture and antigenicity of the vessel wall was preserved. Perfusates of umbilical veins that were transduced with the adenoviral vector containing the α_1-AT transgene were found to contain this protein at a concentration of 13 mg/mL. These were the first in vitro experiments to show that the transduction of vascular cells with an adenoviral vector results in a very high transfection efficiency, and is capable of promoting the expression of transgene-encoding therapeutic proteins that require posttranslational modification.

One of the goals of somatic gene therapy is achieving cell-

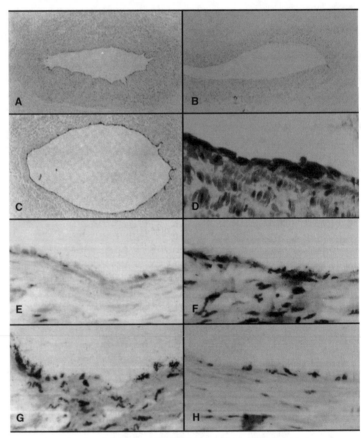

Fig. 4. Adenovirus-mediated transfer of genes to endothelial cells in intact human umbilical veins ex vivo. Veins were exposed for 24 hours to adenovirus RSV β-galactosidase, adenovirus α_1-AT, or adenovirus CFTR. Evaluated for β-galactosidase (A–D) or by in situ hybridization for α_1-AT mRNA (E–H). (A) Uninfected vein magnified 25 times. (B) Same as A, but infected with adenovirus CFTR. (C) Same as A, but infected with adenovirus RSV β-galactosidase. (D) Same as C, but magnified 315 times. (E) Uninfected vein evaluated with α_1-AT antisense probe, magnified 200 times. (F) Same as E, but infected with adenovirus CFTR. (G) Same as E but infected with the adenovirus α_1-AT. (H) Same as G, but with an α_1-AT sense probe. (From Lemarchand, et al.[46] Reprinted with permission.)

specific receptor-mediated gene transfer. Investigators have constructed polylysine-DNA complexes that contain two co-valently linked functional components: a DNA-binding domain and a ligand domain for a specific cell surface receptor.[47] Recognition of the ligand by its appropriate cell surface receptor allows cellular internalization of the complex via receptor-mediated endocytosis. Adenovirus particles are conjugated to these complexes because these conjugates normally lack a specific mechanism to escape lysosomes, and the efficiency of gene transfer is impaired significantly by lysosomal degradation. Preliminary results show that the adenovirus moiety is capable of acting as an endosomolysis agent.[47]

Gene Transfer by Plasmid Vectors

Gene transfer to vascular cells by plasmid DNA constructs has been achieved under a variety of experimental conditions.[48–50] Some, including liposome-mediated gene transfer techniques, show considerable promise. The initial studies of gene transfer by plasmid DNA to vascular cells were undertaken by Powell et al, who used DEAE-dextran or liposomes to mediate gene transfer to endothelial cells, smooth muscle cells, and fibroblasts cultured from human umbilical arteries and veins.[51] The transgene used in these studies was the firefly luciferase gene under control of several different promoters, including that of RSV and that of the tPA type 1 inhibitor. DEAE-dextran–mediated transfections resulted in low-level transient luciferase expression in all three cell types. Liposome-mediated transduction resulted in a fourfold to fivefold greater expression of the RSV-luciferase in endothelial and smooth muscle cells, which remained stable for up to 14 days. The RSV promoter was more effective than the PAI-1 promoter in smooth muscle cells, similar to the PAI-1 promoter in endothelial cells. These studies demonstrated that vascular cells can be transduced by a plasmid liposome conjugate and achieve significant transgene expression.

Plasmid-mediated gene transfer into vascular epithelial cells

In another study of plasmid-mediated gene transfer, Etchberger and Taylor used calcium phosphate coprecipitation to transduce endothelial cells with plasmids containing the neomycin phosphotransferase gene and the chloramphenicol transferase gene under the control of the SV40 promoter.[48] Results showed that endothelial cells in vitro could undergo successful plasmid-mediated transduction and selection with neomycin without effecting the morphology and antigenicity of the endothelial cells.

Plasmid-mediated gene transfer into vascular smooth muscle cells

Vascular smooth muscle cells are an optimal target cell for direct gene transfer. Pickering et al transduced primary cultures of human smooth muscle cells under optimized conditions with a plasmid expressing the firefly luciferase reporter gene or nuclear-targeted β-galactosidase.[49] Vascular smooth muscle cells were derived from normal human internal mammary arteries, arteries containing fragments of atherosclerotic plaque, and lesions of intimal hyperplasia. These investigators also studied liposome-mediated gene transfer of rabbit vascular smooth muscle cells and NIH 3T3 fibroblasts. They noticed some cell loss due to the presence of the liposome-plasmid complex. Although the cells derived from their patients all demonstrated successful gene transfer, as did NIH 3T3 cells, expression in the human vascular smooth muscle cells was markedly reduced. More importantly, transgene expression in cells derived from lesions of intimal hyperplasia was significantly greater than that from vascular smooth muscle cells derived from normal human arteries or primary atherosclerotic plaques. Within a given culture of cells the mitotic index of cells expressing the recombinant gene was significantly higher than that of the total cell population.

The higher transduction of cell efficiency derived from the intimal hyperplasia lesions was thus attributed to their overall higher rate of proliferation in vivo. These results showed that the efficiency of gene transfer by plasmid liposome complexes to cells derived from normal arteries is low. However, the increased rate of proliferation found in certain lesions (eg, atherosclerotic plaques, intimal hyperplasia lesions) appears to facilitate gene transfer by plasmid liposome complexes.

Sendai virus liposome-mediated gene transfer

In vitro experimental studies examining the efficiency of gene transfer to vascular cells by liposome complexes have achieved only limited success. However, this technique frequently causes significant cell injury and death and does not consistently yield high levels of transduction and expression. Recently the Sendai virus (hemagglutinating virus of Japan, HVJ) liposome-mediated gene transfer technique has been shown to be an efficient and nontoxic technique of gene transfer. It uses inactivated HVJ particles to target the DNA-liposome-HVJ complexes to specific cell surface receptors. Morishita et al have characterized the efficiency and suitability of the HVJ method for gene transfer to vascular smooth muscle.[50] The HVJ method showed a tenfold higher efficiency of transduction than did liposomes alone. These investigators also used this method to study vascular angiotensin-converting enzyme (ACE) expression in vascular smooth muscle cells and cultured rat carotid arteries in vitro. In experiments using human ACE cDNA they demonstrated the superiority of the HVJ method over the use of liposomes alone for human smooth muscle cell transduction. More importantly, they successfully transduced a rat carotid artery in culture yielding ACE expression in the media, as detected by immunocytochemistry. Successful gene transfer to the intact rat carotid artery in organ culture supports the potential application of this technique as a powerful tool for somatic gene therapy and the study of vascular wall biology in vivo. Another important finding was that the transduction by the HVJ method did not affect the viability of any of the target cells.

GENE TRANSFER TO VASCULAR CELLS IN VIVO

Cell-mediated vs direct gene transfer

As mentioned earlier, two approaches to achieve gene transfer to vascular cells in vivo are cell-mediated gene transfer and direct gene transfer. Cell-mediated gene transfer offers the distinct advantages of potentially achieving 100% transduction of cells, the ability to determine the effect of the transduction technique on the cell phenotype, and the ability to transplant cells to specific sites in vivo. Disadvantages include a limitation in the number of cell types that can undergo such rigorous manipulation, the risk of contamination and infection in culture, and the potential of complications of the retransplantation procedure. Alternatively, direct gene transfer offers greater simplicity and efficiency from a technical standpoint, but is highly dependent on the availability of efficient transduction techniques. Another disadvantage is the need to maintain site specificity. Nonetheless, rapid advances in gene transfer technology should make the technique of direct gene transfer more widely available in the future.

Experimental Models of Gene Therapy

Vascular Cell-Mediated Gene Transfer In Vivo. In June 1989, Nabel et al published a landmark study in which they documented that genetically modified endothelial cells transplanted into the arterial wall could survive and express the transgene for up to 4 weeks post transplantation.[52] This technique established the potential application of somatic gene therapy in the treatment of patients with cardiovascular disease. An endothelial cell line was first established from an inbred strain of Yucatan mini-pigs in vitro. These endothelial cells were transduced with the BAG retroviral vector, containing the *lacZ* gene, which encodes for β-galactosidase, and the *Tn5* neomycin resistance gene. The presence of this gene allowed transduced cells to be selected in medium containing G418 despite the rather low efficiency of gene transfer. After surgical exposure of the iliofemoral arteries, the preexisting endothelium was denuded with a balloon catheter. The BAG-transfected endothelial cells were then instilled into this arterial segment and allowed to incubate for 30 minutes. At the end of this period antegrade blood flow was restored. Arterial segments were explanted 2 to 4 weeks later, fixed, and stained with X-Gal, a chromogenic galactose substrate. Light microscopy of the fixed arterial wall showed β-galactosidase staining primarily in the luminal endothelial cells. Furthermore, no replication-competent retrovirus could be detected among the endothelial cells cultured in vitro for up to 20 passages.

In a second study of cell-mediated gene transfer, Plautz et al developed a novel approach to eliminate transduced cells containing transgenes whose unregulated expression could cause undesired transformation of the target cell.[53] This study addressed another of the serious safety concerns regarding the application of retroviral vectors to human gene therapy. Overexpression of a transgene encoding a growth factor or angiogenic protein could result in unregulated cell proliferation. Further, incorporation of the retroviral vector into the host genome could cause an insertional mutation. The investigators' approach to this problem was to create a suicide vector that rendered dividing cells sensitive to a specific drug but allowed normal nondividing cells to survive. This was accomplished by the creation of a retroviral vector containing the chicken actin promoter, the polyomavirus enhancer linked to the herpes simplex virus thymidine kinase (*HSV-tk*) gene (Fig. 5; see page 42).

Somatic gene therapy in cardiovascular disease

Figure 5

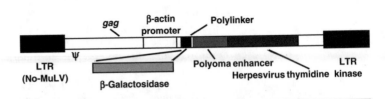

Fig. 5. Suicide retroviral vector, derived from a murine Moloney leukemia virus plasmid that contained an internal chicken β-actin promoter. This plasmid was modified by the insertion of multiple cloning sites, into which was placed the *HSV-tk* gene under the control of a modified polyoma enhancer. The *Escherichia coli* β-galactosidase gene was inserted into this vector under the control of the β-actin promoter. LTR, long-terminal repeat; ψ, retroviral packaging sequence; *gag*, sequences for viral core proteins. (From Plautz, et al.[53] Reprinted with permission.)

Sensitizing dividing endothelial cells to ganciclovir

Thymidine kinase confers sensitivity on the guanosine analogue ganciclovir that inhibits DNA synthesis thereby eliminating proliferating cells. As a marker for transgene expression, the *lacZ* gene also was subcloned into this vector. The investigators established, in vitro, the ability to block β-galactosidase activity in *lacZ*-transduced endothelial cell lines by treatment with ganciclovir. Subsequently, this hypothesis was tested in vivo by direct transfection of the iliofemoral artery in four rabbits. Beginning 1 week after transduction two rabbits received a 4-week regimen of oral ganciclovir. Following this, arterial segments were removed and tested for β-galactosidase activity. Arteries from animals receiving ganciclovir exhibited β-galactosidase activity similar to that seen in the arteries of animals who did not receive the drug, suggesting that the transduced cells attached, expressed recombinant gene, and were not proliferating at the time of ganciclovir administration. To test whether this vector would permit the ganciclovir-mediated killing of replicating cells, a mouse CT26 adenocarcinoma cell line was infected with this suicide vector. After implantation in vivo, the tumors regressed following the administration of ganciclovir.

Human growth hormone fusion gene transfused into pulmonary endothelial cells

In a study by Bernstein et al, pulmonary endothelial cells underwent gene transfer with a human growth hormone fusion gene using calcium phosphate coprecipitation with plasmid DNA.[54] Significant serum levels of human growth hormone were detected following all modes of transplantation. Cells injected beneath the renal capsule resulted in the formation of large cysts that contained high concentrations of human growth hormone. The concentration of growth hormone within these cysts was several thousand times higher than that in serum. These experiments established that genetically modified endothelial cells could form a surface that resulted in a polarized secretion of a new gene product in vivo.

Genetically modified endothelial cells transplanted into capillary beds

The transplantation of genetically modified endothelial cells into a capillary bed has held considerable promise as a technique of somatic gene therapy. Because capillaries constitute more than 80% of the surface area of the circulatory system, they are a logical recipient site for the transplantation of genetically modified endothelial cells in vivo. However, there are a number of potential obstacles to success. Endothelial cells exist in tightly organized layers in which cell density is fixed, and mechanically strong interactions exist between endothelial cells and basement membranes to regulate solute and protein transport. Although the endothelium of muscular arteries has been denuded and reseeded successfully, denudation of capillary endothelium could disrupt important microcirculatory hemodynamics and functions or initiate a vessel wall injury response.

Endothelial cell adhesion to preexisting endothelial monolayers

We undertook a series of in vitro experiments to see if we could circumvent the need for denudation of the capillary endothelium. We tested the hypothesis that the activation of confluent endothelial cell monolayers by cytokines would promote the adhesion and incorporation of endothelial cells seeded onto these monolayers.[55] Cytokines upregulate the expression of a variety of endothelial cell adhesion molecules, result in a loss of junctional integrity between endothelial cells, and increase the metabolic proliferation rates of endothelial cells in vitro and in vivo. In the course of our experiments, in which endothelial cell monolayers were activated by tumor necrosis factor–α, we identified a previously unrecognized capacity of endothelial cells to adhere and incorporate spontaneously into control untreated postconfluent endothelial cell monolayers in vitro. The rate of endothelial cell adhesion onto postconfluent monolayers was rapid; nearly 90% of the seeded endothelial cells became adherent within 6 hours of seeding and nearly 100% were adherent by 24 hours. This resulted in a 50% increase in the monolayer density at 24 hours. Although *lacZ*-transduced endothelial cells became adherent at a significantly slower rate during the first 12 hours, their adhesion was similar to that of the nontransduced endothelial cells by 24 hours. Transmission electron microscopy of the monolayers documented unambiguously that the transduced endothelial cells were fully incorporated into the preexisting monolayer (Fig. 6; see page 44).

Figure 6

In a second series of experiments we documented that this property of spontaneous endothelial cell adhesion and incorporation into preexisting monolayers can occur in vivo and provide a strategy for somatic gene therapy.[55] Radiolabeled microvascular endothelial cells were tracked after being injected intra-arterially into the femoral arteries of the hind limbs of rats (Fig. 7; see page 44). One hour after the femoral artery clamp was removed, 74% of the injected radioactivity was detected in the hind limb. At 28 days 12% of the injected radioactivity was still present in the hind limb. At each time point *lacZ* gene expression was documented within the skeletal muscle capillaries of the injected hind limb. Discrete areas of β-galactosidase activity staining appeared tubular, suggesting incorporation of some of the transduced cells into the capillary wall (Fig. 8; see page 45). Transmission electron microscopy also revealed certain transduced endothelial cells being incorporated into the capillary wall (Fig. 9; see page 46). However, the majority of transduced cells remained within the capillary lumen where they formed multiple areas of focal electron-dense communications with the underlying endothelium of the capillary wall. Although no major surface interaction with

Figure 7

Figure 8

Figure 9

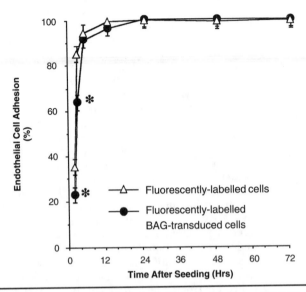

Fig. 6. Rapid adhesion of endothelial cells to postconfluent monolayers in vitro. Mean ± SD. BAG, β-Galactosidase after *gag*. *P <0.05 by Student's *t*-test vs fluorescently labelled nontransduced cells.

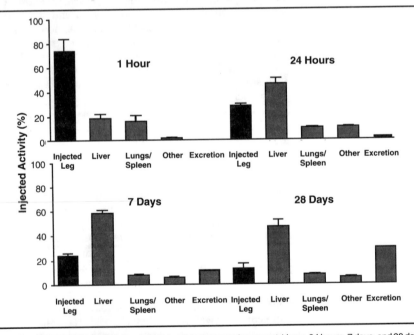

Fig. 7. Distribution of ^{125}I-PKH-95–labelled endothelial cells in tissue and organs at 1 hour, 24 hours, 7 days, and 28 days following the injection of transduced endothelial cells into rat femoral artery. One hour after the clamp was removed 74% of the injected radioactivity was detected in the hind limb, 24 hours following injection 27% of the radioactivity was present in the hind limb, 7 days following injection 24% of the radioactivity was present in the hind limb, and 28 days following injection 12% of the radioactivity was present in the hind limb. The remainder of the radioactivity resided in organs containing a portion of the reticuloendothelial system (liver, lungs, spleen). Selected histologic examination of the liver, lungs, and spleen did not establish definitely whether these cells were viable. (From Messina, et al.[55] Reprinted with permission.)

the capillary basal lamina could be demonstrated, these cells appeared healthy and viable. The long-term effectiveness of this approach to somatic gene therapy will depend on the durability of recombinant gene expression in the endothelium, the life span of the seeded cells, and the long-term consequences of this transplantation technique on the capillary bed and skeletal muscle function.

Vascular smooth muscle–mediated gene transfer

The use of vascular smooth muscle cells for cell-mediated gene transfer also has been explored as a technique of somatic gene therapy.[56,57] Vascular smooth muscle cells offer specific advantages as targets for gene transfer. Like endothelial cells, they exist near the blood-tissue interface but, unlike endothelial cells, which exist in a monolayer, smooth muscle cells form multiple layers and provide a tenfold increase in the number of potential target cells. In addition, abnormal vascular smooth muscle cell proliferation plays a critical role in the development of atherosclerotic plaques and intimal hyperplasia following vascular wall injury.

Lynch et al performed a series of experiments in which rat smooth muscle cells were transduced in culture with a retroviral vector containing the *lacZ* and neomycin resistance genes or the neomycin resistance gene alone.[56] Successful transduction and selection was achieved for both vectors. Subsequently, the left common carotid artery of the rat was denuded by intraluminal passage of a balloon catheter. The retrovirus was instilled at a concentration of 10^6 PFU/mL. Although these experiments showed successful transplantation of the vascular smooth muscle cells into the denuded carotid arteries, the extensive β-galactosidase activity in the control vessels made the results ambiguous. To address this problem a new vector was created containing the human ADA gene. Under these circumstances human ADA can be distinguished readily from endogenous rat ADA by starch gel electrophoresis. Potentially therapeutic levels of human ADA activity were detected in the blood during 6

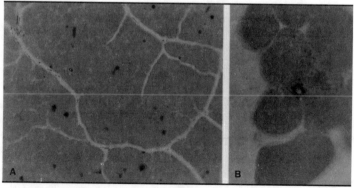

Fig. 8. (A) Photomicrograph of X-Gal–stained cross sections of tibialis anterior muscles. *LacZ*-transduced endothelial cells are in numerous capillaries 1 hour following the injection of transduced endothelial cells (magnified 70 times). Discrete areas of blue (dark patches) are noted only in the regions of capillaries between muscle fibers. (B) *LacZ*-transduced endothelial cell within skeletal muscle capillary 24 hours following injection. (From Messina, et al.[55] Reprinted with permission.)

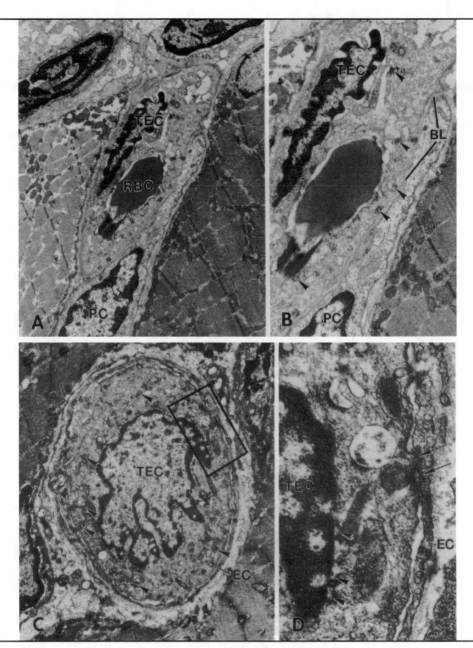

Fig. 9. Electron micrographs of transduced and nontransduced endothelial cells within skeletal muscle capillaries of the rat hind limb. (A) Electron micrograph of a transduced endothelial cell (TEC) incorporated into the wall of a muscle capillary 7 days post transplantation. Note the red blood cell (RBC) within the capillary lumen and pericyte (PC) adjacent to the capillary (magnified 4,350 times). (B) Enlargement of a portion of the capillary in A. The TEC is incorporated fully into the wall and against the capillary basal lamina (BL). Numerous X-Gal–stained granules (arrowheads) are apparent (magnified 7,500 times). (C) Electron micrograph of transduced endothelial cell within the lumen of a muscle capillary 7 days post transplantation. The TEC contains numerous X-Gal–stained granules (arrowheads) and is closely opposed to the normal capillary endothelial cell (EC) (magnified 5,600 times). (D) Enlargement of the rectangular area of C. In many focal regions, the TEC has membrane densities (double arrows) adjacent to the normal EC membrane. Note the X-Gal–stained granules (arrowheads) (magnified 25,000 times). (From Messina, et al.[55] Reprinted with permission.)

Long-term vascular smooth muscle response to retroviral transduction

months of observation, indicating that vascular smooth muscle cell–mediated gene transfer could be used as a technique of systemic gene therapy in humans.

These investigators subsequently determined the long-term biologic response of the smooth muscle to retroviral transduction in vivo.[57] These studies showed that the intimal smooth muscle cell proliferation rate returned to background levels by 28 days following balloon injury. At 12 months no phenotypic differences could be identified between the transduced and normal smooth muscle cells seeded into balloon-injured arteries. The transduced cells continued to express the reporter genes' ADA and the human placental heat-stable alkaline phosphatase. The most critical finding was that the retroviral transduced smooth muscle cells appeared to function normally, suggesting that the cell culture phenotype of vascular smooth muscle cells is reversible once the cell is returned to an appropriate location in vivo. These findings support the use of transduced vascular smooth muscle cells for somatic gene therapy. Potential applications include the local secretion of a specific protein, control of cell proliferation, and moderation of the function and structure of the vascular wall. Furthermore, these authors suggested that cell-mediated gene transfer using vascular smooth muscle cells could be used to seed synthetic vascular grafts or arteriovenous fistulae to secrete a protein in order to achieve a systemic therapeutic effect.

Direct gene transfer

Direct Gene Transfer to Vascular Cells In Vivo. The first report of direct gene transfer into a mammalian target cell came from Palella et al, who constructed an HSV vector that contained the human gene for hypoxanthine phosphoribosyltransferase[58] and transduced portions of the central nervous system using this vector. Direct gene transfer has been achieved in other organs as well. DNA injection of skeletal muscle and receptor-mediated poly-L-lysine–conjugated DNA gene transfer to the liver are two examples. This eliminates the problems of cell harvesting and ex vivo gene transfer as well as the consequences of this manipulation on cell function, cell surface receptors, and the life span of the cell.[12,13]

Nabel et al undertook a series of studies to achieve direct gene transfer into the arterial wall.[59] In their experiments, a retroviral vector was constructed containing the *lacZ* gene controlled by a chicken β-actin promoter and concentrated to achieve titers of 10^4 to 10^6 particles/mL. The pig iliofemoral artery was occluded with a double balloon catheter, which allowed for instillation of the retroviral vector solution into the isolated arterial segment. In this experiment β-galactosidase activity was documented in the arterial wall from 10 days to 21 weeks following transduction. Maximal expression was observed between 2 and 3 months post transduction. Microscopic analysis of the arterial segments showed that the transaction site was not cell-specific, as cells staining positively for β-galactosidase were found across the wall of the iliofemoral artery.

In the same model, these investigators also documented the direct transduction of the arterial wall using a liposome-*lacZ* plasmid complex. The microscopic examination of transduced arteries revealed β-galactosidase activity in the intima, media, and adventitia 4 to 42 days following transduction. No histochemical staining was reported in control arteries. This was the first study to document direct gene transfer to vascular cells in vivo and establish that recombinant gene expression can be achieved at virtually any site within the arterial or venous circulation that is accessible to a percutaneous catheter. This model has obvious application to the management of many vascular diseases.

Adenoviral-mediated gene transfer to endothelial cells

Direct Gene Transfer by Adenoviral Vector. Lemarchand et al transduced the carotid arteries and jugular veins of sheep using adenoviral vectors.[60] These vessels were isolated and infused in vivo with a solution composed of an adenoviral vector containing the *lacZ* gene or the human α_1-AT gene. After a 15-minute incubation the arterial circulation was restored. The contralateral artery or vein was transduced with an adenoviral vector containing the human CFTR and served as a control. Specimens were examined at 1, 7, 14, and 28 days following transduction. Histochemical analysis of arterial segments transfected with the adenoviral vector containing *lacZ* showed cell- and site-specific gene transfer. β-Galactosidase staining was observed only in endothelial cells. The arterial wall was reported to be histologically normal. Importantly, no positive staining was observed in the contralateral artery exposed to the adenovirus CFTR vector or in other tissues except the thyroid, which normally stains positively and was included as a positive control. A more rigorous analysis of greater sensitivity would have to have included DNA PCR or reverse transcriptase PCR to document transduction. Nonetheless, Northern blot analysis confirmed recombinant α_1-AT gene expression at 1, 7, and 14 days post transduction. Northern blot analysis was negative at 28 days.

Adenoviral mediated gene transfer was highly efficient in these studies. Gene expression was maximal at 7 days, after which it declined. These results are consistent with those of other studies in which the same vectors were used for gene transfer to human umbilical endothelial cells in vitro and intact umbilical veins ex vivo.[46] The investigators hypothesized that the loss of gene expression was secondary to endothelial cell injury, a cytocidal immune response induced by heterologous gene products, or degradation of the episomal adenoviral DNA.

Gene transfer into vascular smooth muscle

Lee et al designed a study to determine the efficiency of gene transfer to an injured arterial wall in vivo, the amount or concentration of recombinant protein produced in the arterial wall, the cellular targets of gene transfer, and the duration of recombinant gene expression.[61] For the purpose of this study they used an adenoviral vector containing the β-galactosidase marker gene coupled to an SV40 T-antigen nuclear localization signal. The rat carotid artery underwent balloon injury followed by infusion of the adenoviral vector. Three days following gene transfer recombinant gene expression was assessed quantitatively by measuring β-galactosidase antigen and activity. A concentration-response effect was found between the titer of vector and β-galactosidase expression. Gene transfer was limited to the vascular media where approximately 30% of the smooth muscle cells were transduced. In contrast to the earlier findings of Nabel et al, control arteries infused with vehicle only, a control adenoviral vector, or liposomes with the vector plasmid demonstrated little or no evidence of β-galactosidase expression. The high level of β-galactosidase expression persisted for at least 7 days, but was nearly absent by 14 days. This study established that adenoviral-mediated transfer into an injured artery results in efficient gene transfer into the smooth muscle cells of the media, a pattern different from that reported by other investigators in normal arteries, where only the endothelium was transduced.[60]

In a parallel study, Guzman et al obtained similar results in a model of adenoviral mediated gene transfer into injured rat carotid artery, finding a direct correlation between the duration of incubation and the percentage of positive cells in the neointima.[62] In some of their specimens up to 75% of the medial smooth muscle cells were transduced. The uninjured arteries showed expression limited to the endothelium. Thus, both of these studies showed highly efficient gene transfer into the media of injured arterial walls.

Rome et al examined the anatomic barriers in the arterial wall that influence the distribution of in vivo gene transfer vectors.[63] They used tracer particles the size of liposomes and viral vectors, and subsequently localized these particles using light, fluorescent, and electron microscopy. The model system they employed used a double balloon catheter and varied infusion pressure between 100 and 400 mm Hg. Arterial anatomy imposed a significant constraint on the distribution of in vivo particles. Under both conditions particle delivery occurred only in the intima. Medial smooth muscle cells could be transduced but only under high pressure (5 atm). Thus, in normal elastic arteries, the arterial wall imposes limitations on the penetration of gene transfer vectors, as the media appears to be virtually inaccessible to particles the size of gene transfer reagents delivered by the double balloon catheter protocol. Most atherosclerotic occlusive disease occurs in human muscular arteries but it is not known whether similar findings would occur in these arteries.

Liposome-plasmid vector for direct gene transfer to arterial wall cells

Liposome-Mediated Gene Transfer to the Arterial Wall In Vivo. One advantage of using liposome-mediated gene transfer to the arterial wall is that it eliminates the safety and toxicity concerns of viral vectors. A recent series of experiments explored the feasibility of direct gene transfer of the femoral and coronary arteries of the dog by liposome-mediated gene transfer, demonstrating direct liposome-mediated gene transfer and luciferase expression for up to 3 days.[64,65] The liposome-plasmid solution was introduced by direct exposure and cannulation of the targeted arterial segment. In a subsequent report, the same investigators performed percutaneous catheterization of the coronary arteries, documenting recombinant gene expression between 3 and 5 days in eight of 12 arterial walls, averaging 4.3 pg of luciferase activity.[64] Little activity was noted in 12 control arteries. Using the same technique the investigators showed that the femoral artery could be transduced directly with naked DNA and plasmid-liposome complexes. Unexpectedly, there was little difference in expression between these two groups. These studies established the feasibility of direct gene transfer using a standard cardiovascular interventional technique.

Direct gene transfer to the arterial wall by an exclusively percutaneous strategy was examined further in a rabbit model of normal and balloon-injured atherosclerotic arteries. Using the luciferase gene as a marker, activity was detected in ten of 22 arteries in which direct gene transfer was attempted, including four of ten normal arteries and six of 12 balloon-injured athero-sclerotic arteries. In situ hybridization of transduced atherosclerotic sections documented luciferase gene transcripts in cells limited to the intima. A very low level of gene transfer was documented in the media in the normal and diseased arteries. Barbee et al observed a tenfold higher transgene expression following liposome-gene transfer following balloon injury in dogs.[66]

Proliferative activity and transgene expression

To optimize liposome-mediated gene transfer to the injured arterial wall, Takeshita et al explored the hypothesis that cellular proliferation induced by arterial injury would augment gene expression following liposome-mediated gene transfer.[67] Nondenuded and denuded arterial strips were maintained in organ culture for up to 21 days and subsequently transduced with a mixture of plasmid-encoding firefly luciferase as a marker gene and cationic liposomes. In the nondenuded arteries the culture interval before transduction did not effect transgene expression. In contrast, denuded arteries cultured from 3 to 14 days before transduction yielded a seven- to 13-fold higher transgene expression. A parallel series of experiments was undertaken in vivo using a percutaneous delivery system. Gene expression increased substantially when transfection was performed between 3 and 7 days following angioplasty. The proliferative activity of the neointimal cells, assessed by radiolabeled thymidine incorporation, correlated with the extent of transgene expression. These findings have important implications for the timing of gene transfer to the arterial wall following vessel injury.

Direct transfection of vascular epithelium

Direct Gene Transfer Following the Intravenous Injection of Liposome-DNA Complexes. Brigham et al evaluated cultured pulmonary endothelial cells exposed to a plasmid containing the human growth hormone gene driven by a metallothioneine promoter.[68] After establishing the regulation of recombinant gene expression in vitro by exposure to dexamethasone or cadmium, in vivo experiments using a similar gene construct were undertaken. Twenty-four hours prior to the intravenous injection of the plasmid containing the same metallothioneine promoter, mice were given zinc sulfate, 5,000 ppm in their drinking water. After sacrifice human growth hormone production was assayed in the lungs, livers, and kidneys. The investigators documented human growth hormone only in the lungs. Transgene expression was confirmed by mRNA detection and PCR amplification of the cDNA. These studies showed that transgene expression could be controlled in vivo by the induction of promoter regions.

A second study showing a more widespread transfection of vascular endothelium was reported by Zhu et al. Mixtures of a cytomegalovirus chloramphenicol acetyltransferase plasmid and liposomes were injected into mice.[69] A single intravenous injection of this liposome-plasmid complex into adult mice efficiently transfected vascular endothelium and extravascular tissues, including the lung, spleen, lymph nodes, and bone marrow. Transgene expression was documented for at least 8 or 9 weeks after a single injection. Nearly all of the lung endothelium was shown to be transduced. This relatively simple technique suggests the feasibility of a rapid and reproducible transfer and expression of a gene into the vascular endothelium. If further techniques are developed to achieve target site and cell specificity, they would have considerable applications to gene therapy.

Gene Transfer to Vascular Cells to Treat Specific Cardiovascular Diseases

Seeding endothelial cells onto synthetic vascular grafts

Vascular Graft Dysfunction. One of the most relevant applications of vascular gene therapy is enhancement of the performance and function of vascular grafts. This was recognized at an early stage by Wilson et al, who transplanted genetically modified endothelial cells onto the surface of synthetic vascular grafts.[70] In experimental animals endothelial cell seeding of synthetic vascular grafts with normal endothelium reduces platelet accumulation on the inner surface of the graft and improves graft patency. However, a number of problems have prevented the application of this technique to the management of vascular disease in humans.[48] These include lower rates of surface endothelialization of synthetic vascular grafts by human cells and high thrombosis rates of small-caliber synthetic grafts in vivo. It is hoped that the problem of the thrombogenesis of small-caliber vascular grafts can be addressed by genetically modifying the endothelial cells used for seeding.

In Wilson's study canine endothelial cells were cultured in vitro and transduced with a retrovirus containing the *lacZ* reporter gene. The investigators achieved a variable transduction efficiency, ranging from 5% to 60%. The transduced cells were seeded onto the luminal surfaces of small-caliber dacron vascular grafts. These synthetic grafts were used as carotid interposition grafts in the dog, from whom the endothelial cells were derived. Grafts harvested 5 weeks after implantation showed *lacZ* transgene expression in substantial but variable numbers of cells from each graft. This was the first study to establish that genetically modified endothelial cells could be seeded successfully onto synthetic vascular grafts.

Podrazik et al addressed a fundamental question regarding the application of this biotechnology to the clinical setting[71]: Does the genetic modification of endothelial cells inhibit their capacity to proliferate and, thus, reduce the extent of graft surface endothelialization? The investigators hypothesized that *lacZ*-transduced endothelial cells would achieve the same degree of surface endothelialization as nontransduced endothelial cells

Figure 10

*Impaired capacity of
modified endothelial
cells to endothelialize
a graft surface*

when seeded on expanded polytetrafluoroethylene (ePTFE)
grafts. Endothelial cells were harvested from the jugular vein and
transduced in vitro using the retroviral BAG vector, which
permitted the selection of transduced cells in G418. Nonseeded
ePTFE grafts served as controls. Expression of *lacZ* was noted in
the endothelium derived from five of seven ePTFE grafts following explantation (Fig. 10). Endothelial cells derived from grafts
seeded with nontransduced cells and nonseeded grafts did not
exhibit any β-galactosidase activity. There was substantially less
total graft surface endothelialization in grafts seeded with
transduced endothelial cells than in those seeded with nontransduced cells. Transduced endothelial cells covered only 5% to 12%
of the graft surface whereas nontransduced cells covered more
than 60% of the graft surface. This important finding suggests

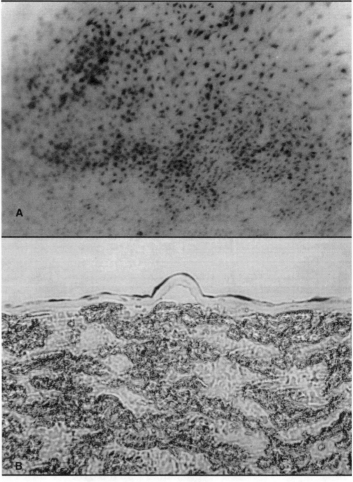

Fig. 10. Photomicrograph of an explant of an ePTFE thoracoabdominal graft that had been
seeded with autologous BAG-transduced endothelium. (A) *En face* preparation showing
diffuse coverage of graft surface by *lacZ*-positive endothelial cells. (B) Longitudinal section
of graft showing continuous monolayer of *lacZ*-positive cells lining the graft.

that transfection with the BAG vector may impair the capacity of transduced endothelial cells to adhere, migrate, or proliferate on the graft surface in vivo. Impaired endothelial cell function could be due to any aspect of the transduction process itself, including exposure to the neomycin analogue G418, random integration of the retrovirus into the endothelial genome altering cell function, or the expression of recombinant proteins by the *lacZ* genes that may induce immune reaction detection of the virally infected cells.

The mechanism responsible for these disappointing results has been explored in a series of in vitro experiments in our laboratory. In one study, BAG-transduced endothelial cells showed reduced rates of cell proliferation and prostacyclin secretion during long-phase cell growth.[72] These observations appear to correlate with the results seen with BAG-transduced cells growing on ePTFE surfaces in vivo. In a more recent study Huber et al tested the hypothesis that canine endothelial cells transduced with the human tPA gene would have a lower rate of adherence to pretreated ePTFE grafts in vitro and in vivo. Additionally it was hypothesized that the transduced endothelial cells would also proliferate at a slower rate on ePTFE grafts in vivo than would nontransduced cells. Somewhat unexpectedly, no significant difference was detected in the rate of adherence or the proliferation of transduced endothelial cells seeded onto ePTFE grafts in vitro. However, by 1 hour after implantation, ePTFE grafts seeded with transduced endothelial cells in vivo had a 20% lower rate of surface coverage than did grafts seeded with nontransduced cells. Thus, the lower rate of surface endothelialization by genetically modified endothelial cells in vivo does not necessarily appear to result from an impaired capacity to adhere or proliferate on the surface of a synthetic graft, per se. The capacity of these cells to remain adherent after exposure to hemodynamic forces in vivo may play a role.

Rapid, efficient repopulation of injured arteries with modified endothelial cells

Conte et al sought to determine whether genetically modified endothelial cells could improve the clinical outcomes of certain procedures, such as endarterectomy, atherectomy, and percutaneous angioplasty.[73] They developed a technique of rapidly and efficiently repopulating injured arteries with genetically modified cells. In a rabbit model, freshly isolated endothelial cells were transduced with a retrovirus using the *lacZ* reporter gene. Transduced cells were then seeded onto the surface of balloon-denuded iliofemoral artery segments at different cell densities. At up to 14 days *lacZ* expression was confirmed in 28 of 32 arteries seeded with genetically modified cells. In the arteries explanted at 4 to 7 days after seeding, 40% to 90% of the surface area was covered by transduced cells; coverage was more variable by 14 days. These studies established the feasibility of creating segments of arterial vessels containing genetically modified cells in a rapid and efficient manner.

Chen et al addressed the problems of early graft thrombosis and accelerated graft atherosclerosis affecting aortocoronary vein grafts.[74] They used direct adenoviral-mediated transfer of the marker gene *lacZ* or soluble vascular cell adhesion molecule

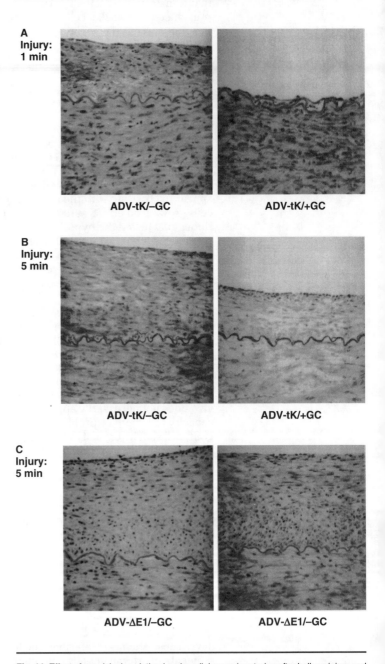

Fig. 11. Effect of ganciclovir on intimal and medial areas in arteries after balloon injury and infection with the *ADV-tk* vector. Representative cross-sections from iliofemoral arteries of pigs (A) injured for 1 minute, then infected with the *ADV-tk* vector and treated with saline (left) or ganciclovir (right), (B) injured for 5 minutes then infected with *ADV-tk* vector and treated with saline (left) or ganciclovir (right), and (C) injured for 5 minutes, then infected with *ADV-ΔE1* and treated with saline (left) or ganciclovir (right). These arteries were examined 3 weeks after injury for gene transfer. (From Ohno T, et al.[75] Reprinted with permission.)

(sVCAM) to transduce segments of porcine jugular vein or human saphenous vein. Jugular veins were interposed as vascular grafts in carotid arteries of four pigs following ex vivo gene transfer with a control or experimental vector. Three days later the vein grafts were explanted and β-galactosidase expression was confirmed by light and transmission electron microscopy. Gene expression occurred in all areas of the vein graft with prominent staining in the adventitia. Expression of sVCAM was confirmed by immunohistochemistry and in situ hybridization.

Intimal Hyperplasia. Ohno et al employed a technique of somatic gene therapy to limit the smooth muscle proliferative response to balloon injury of the artery wall.[75] These investigators hypothesized that local delivery of an antiproliferative agent during peak smooth muscle cell proliferation following balloon angioplasty might limit the subsequent development of intimal hyperplasia. To eliminate dividing cells selectively, they first transduced the vascular wall with a recombinant gene, *HSV-tk*, that converts the nucleoside analogue ganciclovir into an active toxic form. The *tk* enzyme phosphorylates ganciclovir in vivo. It then becomes incorporated into the DNA of dividing cells, inducing chain termination and ultimately causing cell death. The introduction and expression of this recombinant transgene (a suicide vector) into the nondividing cells of the normal arterial wall has no toxic effects.

Eliminating proliferating smooth muscle cells

These investigators constructed an adenoviral vector containing the thymidine kinase gene (*ADV-tk*). In initial studies they optimized and confirmed the transduction of the intima and media by an adenovirus containing a marker gene following balloon injury of the iliofemoral arteries of 1 or 5 minutes' duration. The *ADV-tk* vector was introduced into the arteries by a catheter. Thirty-six hours after injury and transduction, the experimental group received ganciclovir, 50 mg/kg per day for 6 days, and the controls received saline. As an additional control an E1-deleted adenovirus vector without the *tk* gene (ADV-[Δ]E1) was introduced into the injured arteries. These animals were also treated with ganciclovir or saline. Three weeks after balloon injury and adenoviral transduction, quantitative morphometry was used to determine the intimal-to-medial (I-M) surface area ratios. There was a significant reduction in the I-M ratio to 87% 1 minute following injury, and 54% to 59% 5 minutes following injury. In addition, a 40% reduction in the response was noted within 7 days of gene transfer. The results of this short-term study indicate that the introduction of a vector encoding the *HSV-tk* gene coupled with ganciclovir administration limits intimal hyperplasia following arterial balloon injury (Figs. 11, 12; see page 56).

Suicide vector to limit intimal hyperplasia

Figures 11 and 12

Chronic Limb Ischemia. In September 1994 an advisory committee at the National Institutes of Health adopted a proposal in which somatic gene therapy could be used to manage limb ischemia. This was the culmination of a series of experiments by Isner et al.[76,77] These investigators first established the efficacy of direct gene transfer to the arterial wall in a rabbit model by the delivery of naked DNA that had been applied with a thin coat of

Stimulating angiogenesis
and collateralization

hydrogel polymer to the surface of a standard balloon angioplasty catheter. A 1-minute exposure successfully transduced all arteries with luciferase gene expression for up to 14 days. This was a novel method of transferring naked DNA to the arterial wall without the use of liposomes or viral vectors.

In a second series of experiments, vascular endothelial growth factor (VEGF), a heparin-binding endothelial cell–specific mitogen, administered as a single intra-arterial bolus significantly augmented collateral artery development, as measured by angiography, and the number of capillaries per unit area, as measured histologically. Serial angiography disclosed progressive linear extension of the collateral arteries following VEGF therapy.

A protocol by Isner and Walsh recently has been approved for the treatment of patients with intractable ischemic rest pain or ulceration. The technique involves the use of balloon angioplasty catheters whose surfaces are impregnated with a hydrogel containing the VEGF plasmid. The balloon is inflated in an artery near the occlusive lesions. These investigators anticipate that the regional delivery of VEGF will stimulate significant angiogenesis and collateral development to heal the ischemic ulcers or relieve the tissue injury causing the rest pain.

Direct Gene Transfer to the Arterial Wall to Study Vascular Biology

In a series of elegant experiments, Nabel et al explored the use of

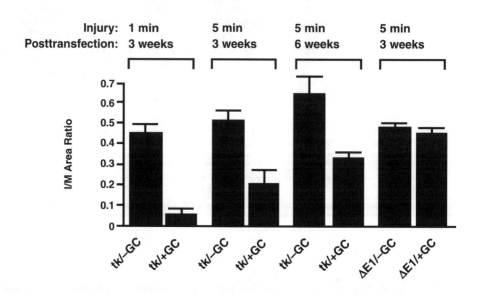

Fig. 12. Measurment of I-M area ratios from arteries infected after a 1-minute injury and 3 weeks post transfection with ADV-*tk* vector and treated with saline or ganciclovir, infected after a 5-minute injury and 3 weeks post transfection with *ADV-tk* vector and treated with saline or ganciclovir, infected after a 5-minute injury and 6 weeks post transfection with *ADV-tk* vector, and treated with saline or ganciclovir, and infected after a 5-minute injury and 3 weeks post transfection with *ADV-ΔE1* vector and treated with saline or ganciclovir. A statistically significant reduction in I-M area ratio is observed in the *ADV-tk*/+GC group compared with the *ADV-tk*/−GC group. (From Ohno, et al.[75] Reprinted with permission.)

Site-specific biologic responses induced by gene transfer

gene transfer to the arterial wall to elucidate the mechanisms of vasculitis and intimal hyperplasia.[63-65] A retroviral vector containing the human class I major histocompatibility complex gene HLA-B7 was used to develop a large-animal model of vasculitis. This study documented for the first time that direct gene transfer into arteries can induce a biologic response in vivo.[78] A PLJ-retroviral vector containing the HLA-B7 cDNA or a *lacZ* gene was constructed and direct gene transfer to the arterial wall in vivo by retroviral vectors and DNA-liposome complexes was undertaken. Histochemical staining showed that the DNA-liposome complex transduced all layers of the arterial wall, with the adventitia demonstrating the highest expression. To determine whether expressed HLA-B7 can induce a specific systemic immune response, the investigators analyzed lymphocytes for cytolytic T-cell activity using a chromium release assay. After in vitro sensitization, cells from the experimental group lysed radionuclide-labeled HLA-B7–positive cells but not negative endothelial cells. As further proof of the induction of the specific biologic response, intense mononuclear infiltration was observed in the arterial wall starting at 10 days after gene transfer and peaking at 2 to 4 weeks following transfer. The inflammation subsided by 10 weeks. An onion-skin pattern of perivascular cuffing and granuloma formation surrounding small capillaries was a prominent finding in sections of the arterial wall.

Unexpectedly, an inflammatory action of lesser intensity was observed in the control arteries that were not exposed to the HLA-B7 vector. No HLA-B7 cDNA was detected by PCR on these sham-infected balloon-injured arteries. According to the investigators this indicated that the immune response to the HLA-B7 antigen induced a systemic sensitivity to the antigens expressed during and after simple balloon injury in the arterial wall. This response in sham-infected arteries had not been seen with any other vector, including that for platelet-derived growth factor. The major finding of this study was that gene transfer to the arterial wall in vivo can induce a potent, site-specific biologic response.

Fibroblast growth factor expression

The development of intimal hyperplasia has been explored by Nabel et al using similar models to determine the role of fibroblast growth factor (FGF) and platelet-derived growth factor (PDGF) in intimal hyperplasia.[79,80] Fibroblast growth factor lacks a classic signal sequence for secretion; thus, an expression vector was created by ligation of the signal sequence from the *hst*/KS3 (FGF-4) gene to the 5'-end of the open-reading frame of the FGF-cDNA in a pMEX neoeukaryotic expression vector. Porcine iliofemoral arteries underwent direct gene transfer with an FGF vector and control arteries were transduced with the *lacZ* gene. Although intimal thickening was seen in arteries exposed to the *lacZ* gene as well as those exposed to the FGF gene, a sixfold greater I-M ratio was observed in the arteries in which the FGF gene was expressed. In several animals multiple capillaries were formed within the neointima. Thus, the expression of secreted recombinant FGF-1 induced intimal hyperplasia and angiogenesis in vivo.

Platelet-derived growth factor expression

Platelet-derived growth factor–β induces cell proliferation in vitro and has been implicated in the induction of intimal hyperplasia in vivo.[79] However, due to the complexity of cellular and protein interactions that follow vessel wall injury in vivo it has been difficult to determine the role of specific gene products as causative factors. The expression of PDGF-β in a porcine model similar to that used in the FGF studies caused intimal hyperplasia within 21 days of transduction of the arterial wall in vivo. This was noted in spite of the relatively low transduction rate of 0.1% to 1% of cells in the artery segment containing the plasma DNA.

During gene transfer with the DNA-liposome complex, the pressure within the artery was controlled at 150 or 350 mm Hg for 30 minutes. No intimal hyperplasia occurred at an instillation pressure of 150 mm Hg but neointimal thickening was observed at an instillation pressure of 350 mm Hg. Immunocytochemistry showed that, at 150 mm Hg, no detectable PDGF-β was detected in the arteries transfected with the *lacZ* gene. Thus, endogenous PDGF-β in the uninjured arteries transduced at low pressures was undetectable. In contrast, arteries transfected with the PDGF-β liposome complex at high pressures revealed immunoreactive proteins in the intimal, medial, and adventitial tissue. These results support the hypothesis that PDGF-β may be important in the development of intimal hyperplasia.

ACE cDNA and renin cDNA

Investigators have suggested that the renin-angiotensin system plays an important role in the regulation of vascular smooth muscle cell (VSMC) growth. Morishita et al transduced VSMCs with the HVJ-liposome method to express ACE, renin cDNA, or both.[81] Their results showed that transfected components of the renin-angiotensin system can modulate VSMC growth through the endogenous production of angiotensin II, and that ACE and renin are limited in determining VSMC renin-angiotensin system activity.

THE FUTURE

The major challenges to the future application of gene therapy to human disease include (1) the development of site- and cell-specific gene transfer techniques; (2) the development of vectors for gene transfer that are efficient and result in durable transgene expression without injury to the target cells; (3) the creation of vectors that allow the regulation of transgene expression, particularly those directing cell-specific expression, inducible promoters, and suicide vectors such as the *ADV-tk*-ganciclovir system; and (4) better characterization of the mechanisms responsible for the fate of recombinant DNA not incorporated into the host cell's chromosomal DNA.

References
1. Vane JR, et al. *N Engl J Med* 1990;323:27-36.
2. Ward PA. *J Lab Clin Med* 1991;118:421-426.
3. Pober JS. *Am J Pathol* 1988;133:426-433.
4. Belloni PN, et al. *Cancer Metast Rev* 1990;8:353-389.
5. Riessen R, et al. *J Am Coll Cardiol* 1994;23:1234-1244.
6. Blaese RM. *Clin Immunol Immunopathol* 1991;61:S47-S55.
7. Kelley WN. *Ann Intern Med* 1991;114:697-698.

8. Miller AD. *Blood* 1990;76:271-278.
9. Mulligan RC. *Science* 1993;269:926-932.
10. Morsy MA, et al. *JAMA* 1993;270:2336-2346.
11. Nabel EG, et al. *Ann Rev Physiol* 1994;56:741-761.
12. Wolff JA, et al. *Science* 1990;247:1465-1468.
13. Wu GY, et al. *Biotherapy* 1991;3:87-95.
14. Wu CH, et al. *J Biol Chem* 1989;264:16985-16987.
15. Felgner PL, et al. *Nature* 1989;337:387-388.
16. Potter H. *Anal Biochem* 1988;174:361-373.
17. Danos O, et al. *Proc Natl Acad Sci USA* 1988;85:6460-6464.
18. Miller AD. *Hum Gene Ther* 1990;1:5-14.
19. Miller DG, et al. *Mol Cell Biol* 1990;10:4239-4242.
20. Quantin B, et al. *Proc Natl Acad Sci USA* 1992;89:2581-2854.
21. Stratford-Perricaudet LD, et al. *J Clin Invest* 1992;90:626-630.
22. Ragot T, et al. *Nature* 1993;361:647-650.
23. Gerard RD, et al. *TCM* 1993;3:171-177.
24. Kolberg R. *J NIH Res* 1992;4:43-44.
25. Kozarsky KF, et al. *Curr Opinion Genet Devel* 1993;3:499-503.
26. Prince GA, et al. *J Virol* 1993;67:101-111.
27. Herz J, et al. *Proc Natl Acad Sci USA* 1993;90:2812-2816.
28. Englehardt JF. *Proc Natl Acad Sci USA* 1994;6186-6200.
29. Faller DV, et al. *J Cell Physiol* 1988;134:47-56.
30. van Zonneveld AJ, et al. *Proc Natl Acad Sci USA* 1988;85:5525-5530.
31. Lee ME, et al. *J Biol Chem* 1990;265:10446-10450.
32. Wilson DB, et al. *Mol Cell Biol* 1990;10:4854-4862.
33. Zwiebel JA, et al. *Science* 1989;243:220-222.
34. Zwiebel JA, et al. *Biochem Biophys Res Commun* 1990;170:209-213.
35. Wilson JM, et al. *Trans Assoc Am Phys* 1989;102:139-147.
36. Dichek DA, et al. *Blood* 1991;77:533-541.
37. Dichek DA. *Mol Biol Med* 1991;8:257-266.
38. Kahn ML, et al. *Circ Res* 1992;71:1508-1517.
39. Jaklitsh, MT, et al. *J Cell Physiol* 1993;154:207-216.
40. Lee SW, et al. *J Biol Chem* 1992;267:13020-13027.
41. Podrazik RM, et al. *Ann Surg* 1992;216:446-453.
42. Xu XM, et al. *J Clin Invest* 1993;91:1843-1849.
43. Ramos TK, et al. *Surg Forum* 1992;43:334-336.
44. Yao S-N, et al. *Proc Natl Acad Sci USA* 1991;88:8101-8105.
45. Schneider MD, et al. *Circulation* 1993;88:1937-1942.
46. Lemarchand P, et al. *Proc Natl Acad Sci USA* 1992;89:6482-6486.
47. Curiel DT, in Melnick JL (ed). *Progress in Medical Virology*. Basel, Karger, 1993, pp 1-18.
48. Etchberger KJ, et al. *Ann Vasc Surg* 1989;3:123-126.
49. Pickering JG, et al. *Circulation* 1994;89:13-21.
50. Morishita R, et al. *Hypertension* 1993;21:894-899.
51. Powell JT, et al. *Eur J Vasc Surg* 1992;6:130-134.
52. Nabel EG, et al. *Science* 1989;244:1342-1344.
53. Plautz G, et al. *New Biol* 1991;3:709-715.
54. Bernstein SC, et al. *FASEB J* 1990;4:2665-2670.
55. Messina LM, et al. *Proc Natl Acad Sci USA* 1992;89:12018-12022.
56. Lynch CM, et al. *Proc Natl Acad Sci USA* 1992;89:1138-1142.
57. Clowes MM, et al. *J Clin Invest* 1993;93:644-651.
58. Nabel EG, et al. *Science* 1990;249:1285-1288.
59. Palella TD, et al. *Gene* 1989;80:137-144.
60. Lemarchand P, et al. *Circ Res* 1993;72:1132-1138.
61. Lee SW, et al. *Circ Res* 1993;73:797-807.
62. Guzman RJ, et al. *Circulation* 1993;88:2838-2848.
63. Rome JJ, et al. *Arterioscler Thromb* 1994;14:148-161.
64. Chapman GD, et al. *Circ Res* 1992;71:27-33.
65. Lim CS, et al. *Circulation* 1991;83:2007-2011.
66. Barbee RW, et al. *Biochem Biophys Res Comm* 1993;190:70-78.
67. Takeshita S, et al. *J Clin Invest* 1994;93:652-661.
68. Brigham KL, et al. *Am J Respir Cell Mol Biol* 1993;8:209-213.

69. Zhu N, et al. *Science* 1993;209:261-263.
70. Wilson JM, et al. *Science* 1989;244:1344-1346.
71. Podrazik RM, et al. *Surg Forum* 1993;44:334-337.
72. Brothers TE, et al. *Surg Forum* 1989;41:337-339.
73. Conte MS, et al. *Circulation* 1994;89:2161-2169.
74. Chen SJ, et al. *Circulation* 1994;89:1922-1928.
75. Ohno T, et al. *Science* 1994;265:781-784.
76. Takeshita S, et al. *J Clin Invest* 1994;93:662-670.
77. Riessen R, et al. *Hum Gene Ther* 1993;4:749-758.
78. Nabel EG, et al. *Proc Natl Acad Sci USA* 1992;89:5157-5161.
79. Nabel EG, et al. *J Clin Invest* 1993;91:1822-1829.
80. Nabel EG, et al. *Nature* 1993;362:844-846.
81. Morishita R, et al. *J Clin Invest* 1993;91:2580-2585

Supported by NIH HL51184 and VA Merit
Review Grants.

III Advances in Gene Therapy of Cancer

James S. Economou, MD, PhD
Eric M. Toloza, MD, PhD

INTRODUCTION

Table 1

As of July 1994, cancer-related gene transfer protocols have comprised 68% of clinical trials of human gene therapy worldwide (Table 1). This preponderance of effort directed at neoplastic disease relative to diseases resulting from inherited disorders (eg, adenosine deaminase deficiency, cystic fibrosis) or viral infections (eg, the acquired immunodeficiency syndrome) is the result of dramatic advances in our understanding of the molecular genetics of cancer coupled with the failure of conventional therapy to treat many cancers effectively.

Gene marker trials

Most of these gene-marking trials involve malignancies that can be treated successfully by available cytotoxic drugs. These include childhood leukemias and Hodgkin's disease, and malignancies that require bone marrow rescue after high-dose drug regimens. These gene-marking trials are designed to study the biology of bone marrow reconstitution and determine the reason for the recurrence of leukemia after autologous bone marrow transplantation. A few marking trials are attempting to determine the survival and distribution of reinfused autologous tumor infiltrating lymphocytes and identify the subpopulation of lymphocytes that is able to infiltrate tumors.

Therapeutic trials

Therapeutic clinical trials involve the many cancers for which conventional therapies have not been as successful. These include brain tumors, breast cancer, colorectal cancer, melanomas, neuroblastomas, lung cancer, and ovarian cancer. This section will discuss not only these early phase I trials but recent preclinical findings that have potential application toward the treatment of cancer.

BASIC STRATEGIES

Cancer gene therapies

Currently there are three strategies being tested in cancer gene therapy: Replacement of a missing or defective gene, such as a mutated tumor suppressor gene; inhibition of the overexpression of activated or amplified oncogenes; and the introduction of a functional gene into a cell to effect a desired result, such as the introduction of a cytokine or antigen to stimulate an immune response or the introduction of an enzyme to increase drug sensitivity.

Protocol design criteria

The design of any successful cancer gene therapy protocol requires the identification of the correct combination of three factors for each type of cancer: the gene to be transferred, the gene delivery method, and the target cells to be modified. To choose a particular component several technical issues must be considered, including the efficiency of transduction, the specificity of cell targeting and gene expression, the duration of gene expression, the level of gene expression, the effect on normal cells, and the ability to establish systemic immunity. While the overall goal is to eradicate all malignant cells, a low transduction efficiency may be acceptable if a local bystander effect or

Table 1. Recombinant DNA Advisory Committee–
Approved Gene Marking Therapy Clinical Trials as of July 1994

Type of Cancer	Target Cells	Class of Gene Transferred	No. of Protocols
Advanced cancer (NOS*)	TILs	Marker gene (*neo'*)	1
	TILs	Cytokine (*TNF*)	1
	Tumor cells	Cytokine (*IL-2, TNF*)	2
	Tumor cells	Surface antigen (*HLA-B7*)	2
	Fibroblasts	Cytokine (*IL-4*)	1
	Hematopoietic stem cells	Marker gene (*neo'*)	3
	Hematopoietic stem cells	Drug resistance (*MDR-1*)	1
Brain tumor	Tumor cells	Antisense (*IGF-1*)	1
	Tumor cells	Suicide gene (*HSV-tk*)	5
	Tumor cells	Cytokine (*IL-2, IFN-γ*)	2
	Fibroblasts	Cytokine (*IL-2*)	1
	Hematopoietic stem cells	Marker gene (*neo'*)	3
Breast cancer	Hematopoietic stem cells	Marker gene (*neo'*)	2
	Hematopoietic stem cells	Drug resistance (*MDR-1*)	1
Colorectal cancer	Tumor cells	Surface antigen (*HLA-B7*)	1
	Fibroblasts	Cytokine (*IL-2*)	1
Leukemias/lymphomas	Hematopoietic stem cells	Marker gene (*neo'*)	8
Lung cancer	Tumor cells	Antisense (*ras*)	1
	Tumor cells	Tumor suppressor (*p53*)	1
	Tumor cells	Cytokine (*IL-2*)	1
Melanoma	TILs	Marker gene (*neo'*)	2
	Tumor cells	Surface antigen (*HLA-B7*)	1
	Tumor cells	Cytokine (*IL-2, IL-4, IFN-γ*)	6
Ovarian cancer	Tumor cells	Suicide gene (*HSV-tk*)	1
	Hematopoietic stem cells	Drug resistance (*MDR-1*)	1
Renal cancer	TILs	Marker gene (*neo'*)	1
	Tumor cells	Cytokine (*IL-2, GM-CSF*)	3

*NOS = not otherwise specified.

systemic immunity can be achieved. The specificity of cell targeting and gene expression is important when the transferred genes would be toxic to normal cells. A high level of gene expression may be more important for secreted gene products than for gene products that remain within the tumor cells. Transient gene expression also may be acceptable if the duration of gene expression exceeds the time period required to kill all tumor cells. Toxicity to normal cells may be avoided with the use of tumor-specific promoters. Finally, the achievement of systemic tumor immunity (eg, by stimulation with cytokine-producing tumor cells) may produce a more durable antitumor effect than strategies incorporating antisense constructs or suicide genes.

Choice of Target Cells

Cell modification goals

Possible target cells include not only tumor cells and immune effector cells, but surrounding normal tissue. The genetic modification of tumor cells may result in enhanced immunogenicity and, ultimately, vaccines, and increase drug or radiation sensitivity of the tumor cells or reversion of the malignant phenotype. Immune effector cells, such as tumor infiltrating lymphocytes (TILs) or macrophages, could be gene-modified to have increased antitumor efficacy or enhanced tumor–immune cell interaction. Finally, the modification of normal cells, such as hematopoietic stem cells, could provide for greater resistance to the toxicity of chemotherapy.

Choice of Delivery Methods

Various methods are available to deliver novel genes into target cells. Physical methods, such as calcium phosphate precipitation, electroporation (the use of an electric field to reversibly permeabilize cells), direct microinjection, and particle bombardment, may be suitable for introducing DNA into established cell lines in vitro but, for the most part, are of low efficiency and often are impractical for in vivo applications. Liposome-mediated gene transfer is suitable for gene transfer in vivo and has been used successfully clinically. Biologic vectors in the form of replication-defective viruses are more efficient. Retroviral vectors are the best characterized and most commonly used. These vectors have the advantage of being able to integrate into the cell genome and result in the permanent transduction of the target cells. However, retroviral vectors are generated at low titer, are able to infect only dividing cells with low transduction efficiency, and result in variable expression levels. In addition, although retroviral-mediated transduction might result in permanent integration of the foreign gene into the target cell, the promoter used to drive the transcription of the foreign gene must be selected carefully.

Retroviral vectors

Adenovirus vectors

Recombinant adenovirus vectors can be produced at high titer, infect nondividing cells at high efficiencies, and result in high expression levels. However, adenovirus vectors are nonintegrative and, therefore, result in only transient expression of the inserted gene over a few weeks to months. Moreover, adenovirus-transduced cells elicit an immune response in vivo that results in their destruction and the production of neutraliz-

Adeno-associated virus vectors

ing antiviral antibodies that prevents subsequent vector administration.

Adeno-associated virus vectors are able to integrate multiple copies into the target cell genome. However, the full potential of these vectors for gene transfer in vitro and in vivo has not been determined. Current adeno-associated virus vector generation methods are cumbersome and require the development of packaging cell lines and better purification techniques.

Choice of Therapeutic Gene

Therapeutic genes fall into six classes: oncogenes, tumor suppressor genes, suicide genes, cell surface antigens, cytokine genes, and multiple drug resistance genes. Oncogene inhibition or tumor suppressor gene replacement would correct the abnormal malignant phenotype. Suicide genes would provide transduced tumor cells with enzymatic machinery to convert otherwise nontoxic precursors into toxic metabolites. Cell surface protein genes and cytokine genes may result in better tumor–immune cell interaction and stimulation of the immune response. Hematopoietic stem cells could be rendered resistant to the systemic toxicity of chemotherapeutic agents upon transduction with a multiple drug resistance gene.

TUMOR-INFILTRATING LYMPHOCYTES

Gene-marker studies

Almost all of the gene therapy experiments to date that involve tumor-infiltrating lymphocytes have been gene-marking studies to map the fate of reinfused TILs that had been expanded ex vivo from tumor biopsy specimens. The first experiments, which began in May 1989, involved the transduction of TILs with the neomycin-resistance (*neo*^{r}) gene using a retrovirus vector. The TILs were then followed to determine whether they localized to the tumor.[1-3] A small percentage of the TILs were, indeed, found in the tumor by polymerase chain reaction. In addition, gene-modified TILs were found in the peripheral blood for up to 6 months and in the tumors for up to 2 months.[1] There is in vitro evidence that lymphocytes suffer a relative loss in their ability to localize to tumors following the insertion of a foreign gene.[4] Clinical response rates also were variable, unpredictable, and limited to tumor type.

Transduction of cytokine genes

More recent animal studies are evaluating the feasibility of gene transfer of cytokines, such as interleukin-2 (IL-2) and tumor necrosis factor–α (TNF-α) into the TILs to increase their antitumor effects.[5,6] Humans cannot tolerate these cytokines at the dosage (per kilogram body weight) necessary to effect tumor regression in mice, although intratumoral administration or isolated limb perfusion with large doses of TNF have resulted in local tumor regression in some patients. Cytokine-transduced TILs could produce high local concentrations within tumors, thereby avoiding systemic toxicity. However, phase I clinical trials, which began in January 1991, have been hampered by poor transduction efficiencies into the human TILs, low gene expression levels, and the silencing of gene expression in the TILs.[7]

Hwu et al[7] are attempting to transfer a chimeric antibody/T-

*Transduction of
antibody receptor genes*

cell–receptor gene into TILs in order to increase the antigen specificity of these lymphocytes.[8] Transduced TILs modified with a chimeric antiovarian antibody/T cell–receptor gene were able to specifically lyse ovarian cancer cells in a major histocompatibility complex (MHC)-independent fashion. Yannelli et al[9] are coculturing cytokine-transduced tumor cells with TILs in vitro in order to achieve antigen-specific TILs that could then be expanded and reinfused into patients for potentially improved targeting to remaining tumors.

ONCOGENE THERAPY

*Transduction of
antisense K-ras*

Figure 1

Figure 2

The *ras* oncogene is one of the most frequently activated oncogenes in human cancers, with an incidence of up to 30% in non–small cell lung cancers and up to 75% in human pancreatic cancers.[10,11] Retroviral-mediated transduction of antisense K-*ras* into a human lung cancer cell line, which has mutations in both endogenous *ras* alleles, has resulted in decreased tumorigenicity in *nu/nu* mice (Fig. 1).[12] Georges et al[13] demonstrated that the intratracheal instillation of antisense K-*ras* using a retroviral vector prevented the growth of human lung cancer cells in up to 90% of *nu/nu* mice.

Another approach involves the introduction of ribozymes directed against oncogene mRNA (Fig. 2). Ribozymes are RNA molecules designed to bind and cleave specific mRNA. One experimental effort, using a ribozyme that targets the *ras* oncogene message, resulted in abrogated tumorigenicity of a melanoma model and reduced invasiveness of a bladder carcinoma model.[14,15] Even mutant ribozymes, which lack nuclease activity but retain antisense activity, yield a partial decrease of *ras* mRNA. However, the antitumor effect of the *ras* ribozyme against melanoma was not complete. Many cancers may have

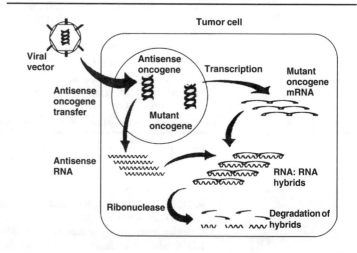

Fig. 1. Antisense oncogene therapy. The expressed antisense RNA then hybridizes to the activated mutant oncogene mRNA. This RNA:RNA hybrid is then degraded by cellular ribonucleases and the malignant phenotype is reversed.

several activated oncogenes. For melanoma, the *fos* and *jun* oncogenes also may be activated; thus, interdiction of only one may have limited success. In fact, another ribozyme against the *fos* oncogene has been reported to result in a reversal of cisplatin resistance.[16]

Robinson-Benion et al,[17] who are attempting to optimize this form of gene therapy, are cotransfecting antisense RNA against the endogenous activated tumor-promoting oncogene as well as an exogenous antisense-resistant form of the oncogene into tumor cells. This exogenous antisense-resistant oncogene copy expresses a gene product with wild-type oncogene activity but contains a mutation that prevents its transcript from binding to the antisense RNA and being degraded. While the antisense RNA inhibits endogenous tumor-promoting oncogene expression, the cotransfected antisense-resistant oncogene could restore serum-regulated DNA synthesis and normalize growth patterns in the tumor cells. Unfortunately, this approach does not result in the elimination of nontransduced tumor cells nor does it confer systemic immunity.

TUMOR SUPPRESSOR GENE THERAPY

The p53 gene

Introduction of the wild-type tumor suppressor gene into tumor cells, in which both endogenous alleles have been mutated or deleted, may reverse the malignant phenotype. One such tumor suppressor gene, *p53*, codes for a gene product that is a nuclear protein capable of arresting the cell cycle. Loss of both *p53* alleles through point mutation, deletion, or rearrangement results in a transformation of normal cells to malignant cells. Mutations in *p53* often are associated with overexpression or accumulation of the aberrant gene product. Mutations of *p53* have been found to occur at high frequency in a variety of human cancers.

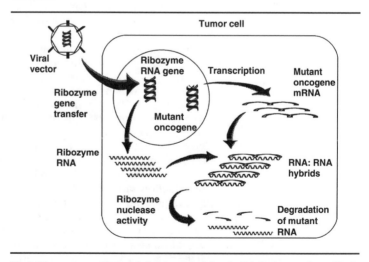

Fig. 2. Ribozyme gene therapy. A ribozyme gene is inserted into the tumor cell, specifically binds to mRNA from the activated oncogene, and the nuclease activity of the ribozyme cleaves the oncogene mRNA. The malignant phenotype is reversed.

Wild-type p53 *gene*

Fujiwara et al[18] were able to induce apoptosis in non–small cell lung cancer cells by using retrovirus vector–mediated transduction of the wild-type *p53* gene into these cells. Preliminary experiments by these investigators have shown that intratracheal instillation of the retrovirus-*p53* vector prevented the growth of established human lung cancer tumors in *nu/nu* mice. Similar results were reported in human osteosarcoma and peripheral neuroepithelioma cells transduced with a retrovirus containing the *p53* gene.[19] Experiments in which transduced cells were mixed with nontransduced cells resulted in a slowed growth rate in the nontransduced cells.[20] This observation suggests the occurrence of a bystander effect, although the mechanism has not been characterized. Fujiwara et al[21] introduced the wild-type *p53* gene into the same cells by using an adenovirus vector and were able to markedly increase the sensitivity of these lung cancer cells to cisplatin. A clinical trial using an adenovirus-*p53* vector in lung cancer has recently been approved by the Recombinant DNA Advisory Committee (RAC).

nm23 *genes*

The *DCC* (deleted in colorectal carcinoma), *RB-1* (retinoblastoma), and *nm23* genes also fall within this class of targeted genes. Loss of the *DCC* gene, which codes for a cell-adhesion molecule–like protein, is thought to be an early event in the development of colon cancer.[22] The *nm23* gene encodes a nucleotide diphosphate kinase and is considered to be a metastasis-suppressor gene. The replacement of this gene into some tumors has suppressed metastases in animal models.[23]

SUICIDE GENE THERAPY

HSV-tk *gene*

Figure 3

The herpes simplex virus–thymidine kinase (*HSV-tk*) gene has been the most commonly studied suicide gene. This enzyme can specifically bind and phosphorylate nucleoside analogues, such as acyclovir and ganciclovir, whereas the endogenous mammalian thymidine kinases cannot (Fig. 3). Replicating cells that express *HSV-tk* incorporate phosphorylated ganciclovir during DNA synthesis, causing its arrest and the death of the cell. Tumors surrounded by nondividing cells, such as those in the brain, are ideally suited for gene therapy using this approach.[24-26] One group of investigators successfully used retrovirus packaging cell lines, which continuously produced retrovirus vectors containing the *HSV-tk* gene, to treat brain tumors. They were able to cause the complete regression of cerebral gliomas in the rat after the injection of murine fibroblasts producing the retrovirus-*HSV-tk* vectors stereotactically into the tumor.[26,27] Other investigators have been able to selectively kill liver metastases, lung cancer cells, hepatocellular carcinomas, and lymphomas after transduction with retrovirus vectors carrying the *HSV-tk* gene and the systemic administration of ganciclovir.[28-32] A clinical trial using retrovirus–*HSV-tk* packaging cell lines injected into glioma patients began in December 1992, and three others that also target brain tumors have been approved, including two protocols aimed at pediatric astrocytoma patients. A fifth clinical trial involving transfer of the *HSV-tk* gene has been approved for the treatment of ovarian cancer.

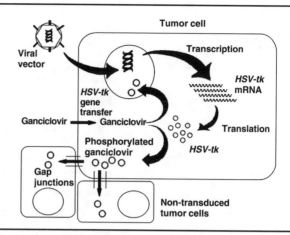

Fig. 3. Suicide gene therapy using herpes simplex virus–thymidine kinase (*HSV-tk*) gene. Viral-mediated transfer of *HSV-tk* into the tumor cell is later followed by systemic ganciclovir administration. The *HSV-tk* phosphorylates the ganciclovir, which causes cell cycle arrest during DNA synthesis. The phosphorylated ganciclovir can also be passed into adjacent nontransduced tumor cells via gap junctions and cause bystander cell cycle arrest.

This delivery method would most likely result in low transduction efficiency, but a bystander effect has been shown to result in the death of surrounding nontransduced tumor cells. This phenomenon is due to the passage of phosphorylated ganciclovir from the transduced cells to adjacent nontransduced tumor cells via gap junctions. Complete tumor regression can be achieved in animal models with transduction efficiency as low as 10%.[26] However, this phenomenon is limited to tumor cells in proximity to the *HSV-tk*–expressing cells and does not result in systemic immunity.

The *Escherichia coli* cytosine deaminase (*cd*) gene is another suicide gene that is under investigation.[33-35] Normal mammalian cells do not express this gene. The relatively nontoxic 5-fluorocytosine (5-FC) can be metabolized to the highly toxic 5-fluorouracil by tumor cells transduced with the *cd* gene (Fig. 4; see page 70). The elimination of established *cd*-expressing tumors in mice after systemic treatment with 5-FC has been demonstrated without significant toxicity to the host.[36] Additionally, it has been reported that these mice were specifically resistant to subsequent rechallenge with unmodified parental tumor cells.

CELL SURFACE ANTIGEN–MEDIATED TUMOR VACCINES

The insertion of a gene encoding for a cell surface antigen is one of two strategies to enhance the immunogenicity of tumor cells (Fig. 5; see page 70). The other is the insertion of cytokine genes. The first trials of these genes involved the non–virus-mediated transduction of tumors in vivo and began in June 1992. The *HLA-B7* gene was delivered into melanoma cells via liposomes injected directly into the tumor. The *HLA-B7* antigen is expressed transiently on the cell surface with the goal of inducing an allogeneic and tumor-specific immune response. Preliminary data on three

Figure 4

Figure 5

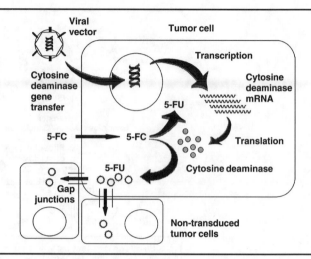

Fig. 4. Suicide gene therapy using the *Escherichia coli* cytosine deaminase (*cd*) gene. Vector-mediated transfer of *cd* into the tumor cell is later followed by systemic administration of nontoxic 5-FC. The 5-FC is then converted by cytosine deaminase in the cell to the toxic 5-fluorouracil (5-FU), which kills the tumor cells. The 5-FU can also kill adjacent tumor cells.

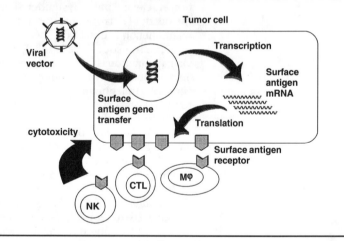

Fig. 5. Antigen gene therapy. A foreign cell surface antigen gene is transferred and expressed by tumor cells. The immune response to this foreign antigen enhances its recognition of tumor-specific antigens.

patients show one patient with regression of the injected tumor and other, noninjected, tumors.[37] The protocol has been amended to include the addition of the β_2-microglobulin gene in order to enhance the immunogenicity of the tumor cells, and has been expanded to include treatment of colorectal cancer metastases to the liver.

Insulin-like growth factor–I

Although not a true cell surface antigen, insulin-like growth factor–I (IGF-I) can be placed in this class of genes. This growth factor appears to make some tumors less immunogenic. The insertion of an antisense IGF-I gene into IGF-I–producing tumor cells inhibited IGF-I production and resulted in the rejection of these cells in animal models as well as nontransduced tumor cells elsewhere in the animals.[38] A clinical trial has been approved to study the introduction of antisense IGF-I into brain tumor patients.

CYTOKINE-MEDIATED TUMOR VACCINES

The administration of recombinant cytokines, especially when delivered directly into tumor sites, has resulted in significant antitumor effects. However, cytokines have systemic side effects and short serum half-lives, which limit their therapeutic index. Several investigators are attempting to enhance the host antitumor response by introducing cytokines into tumor cells,[39,40] or even other cells, such as fibroblasts, when tumor cells cannot be grown.[41,42] However, one group has demonstrated that the induction of an antitumor response is more effective by a cytokine-secreting tumor cell than by cytokine-secreting fibroblasts.[43]

Cytokines can be introduced into tumor cells in vivo, in which case the gene is somehow delivered directly into the tumor, systemically with the hope of targeting to the tumor, or ex vivo, in which case the tumor is explanted and the gene transferred to the tumor cells in culture (Fig. 6). In the former, the cytokine-producing transduced tumor cells would potentially sentence not only themselves but other nearby nontransduced tumor cells to the resulting enhanced antitumor activity of immune mediators. With the ex vivo approach, the irradiated transduced tumor cells could then be reinjected close to accessible established tumors to exploit this bystander effect or at remote sites to act as vaccines. Either method would then lead to the highly localized secretion of therapeutic levels of the cytokine, recruitment of

Figure 6

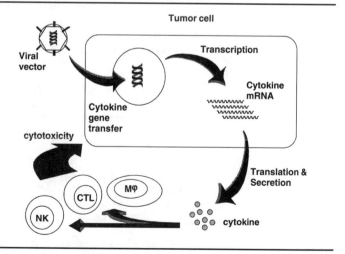

Fig. 6. Cytokine gene therapy. Cytokine-transduced tumor cells attract an inflammatory infiltrate (NK, CTL, Mφ) that destroys tumor cells. A by-product of this interaction is the generation of tumor immunity.

immune cells into the tumor site, and enhancement of tumor-specific antigen presentation. These events could educate the immune cells and confer systemic immunity to the patient against any concurrent micrometastatic disease. Over the past few years, several animal models have shown decreased tumorigenicity of tumor cells transduced with various cytokines, including IL-2, IL-4, IL-7, TNF-α, interferon-γ (IFN-γ), and granulocyte-macrophage colony-stimulating factor (GM-CSF).

Clinical trials with transduced cytokine genes

The majority of the therapeutic gene therapy clinical protocols involve cytokine-mediated tumor vaccines, with eight approved trials and at least six others pending approval. The first trial began in October 1991 with retrovirus-mediated transduction of melanoma with TNF, but the most commonly used cytokine is IL-2. Clinical trials using IFN-γ or IL-4 are under way, and another, using GM-CSF, has been approved.

Interleukin-2 Gene Therapy

Of the various cytokines, IL-2 has been the most commonly studied. Vieweg et al[44] demonstrated that IL-2 gene–modified prostate tumor cells were capable of causing a regression of subcutaneous established tumors in a rat model. The rats that rejected the tumors were also protected from subsequent challenges of unmodified tumor cells. This abrogated tumorigenicity and induction of systemic immunity also have been demonstrated for weakly immunogenic, 3-methylcholanthrene-induced tumor cells and nonimmunogenic murine fibrosarcomas (FSAs) following IL-2 transduction.[45,46] Vaccination with IL-2–producing tumor cells also has caused the regression of metastatic lesions.[47]

Resistance to tumor growth

Initially, this resistance to tumor growth was reported to be natural killer (NK) cell–mediated.[48] However, the recruitment of tumor-specific cytotoxic T lymphocytes was reported with repeated vaccination and required for the establishment of protective immunity.[48] Rosenthal et al[49] reported that CD8+ cytotoxic T cells mediated rejection of murine FSA (CMS-5) cells retrovirally transduced with IL-2 and IFN-γ. Similarly, a renal carcinoma cell line was reported as having decreased tumorigenicity after transfection with IL-2 and/or IFN-α even in T-cell–depleted mice.[50] At least in the case of CMS-5 FSA cells, specialized antigen-presenting cells, rather than T-helper cells, are felt to be needed to induce a cytolytic T-cell response against MHC class I antigens on these tumor cells since they are MHC class II–negative.[51]

Recently, adenovirus-mediated IL-2 gene transfer into murine mastocytoma cells resulted in an 80% loss of tumorigenicity in syngeneic mice, with evidence of a bystander effect, and also resulted in systemic immunity in 50% of the mice.[52] Splenocytes were found to be able to transfer the immunity to syngeneic mice.

Interleukin-3 Gene Therapy

More recently, the retroviral-mediated transduction of the murine IL-3 gene into FSA cells resulted in abrogated tumorigenicity and tumor-specific systemic immunity.[53] This rejection was effected via both paracrine pathways to induce a granulocyte response as well as by autocrine pathways to increase MHC class I and CD44 antigen expression. Furthermore, splenocytes from the immunized mice could cause regression of established parental tumors in SCID mice following adoptive transfer.

Interleukin-4 Gene Therapy

Interleukin-4–transfected murine renal tumor cells have been shown to be rejected in animals via a T-cell–dependent process.[54] Systemic immunity was also established against parental tumor cells, which was tumor-specific and CD8+ T-cell–mediated. In contrast, Tepper et al[55] demonstrated that the antitumor effect against IL-4–transduced plasmacytoma and melanoma cells could be abolished with an antibody against granulocytes.

Interleukin-6 Gene Therapy

Interleukin-6 has variable effects on IL-6–producing tumor cells. Porgador et al[56] reported decreased tumorigenicity of IL-6–transduced lung carcinoma cells and T-cell–dependent systemic immunity against rechallenge and metastases from nontransduced parental cells. Similar results were observed with IL-6–transduced murine FSA cells.[57]

Interleukin-7 Gene Therapy

Our group has extensively studied IL-7 transduction. The tumorigenicity of murine FSA cells in syngeneic mice was abrogated after ex vivo transduction with retrovirus vectors carrying the murine IL-7 gene.[58,59] The genetically modified FSA cells remained as tumorigenic as unmodified parental FSA cells in T-cell–depleted mice. Moreover, immunologically intact mice that had rejected the IL-7–producing FSA cells were specifically immune to rechallenge with parental FSA cells. Infiltrating lymphocytes, predominantly CD8+, from the IL-7–producing tumors, had increased cytotoxicity against parental FSA cells. Hock et al[60] previously reported similar findings with a plasmacytoma cell line transduced with the IL-7 gene, although they reported recruitment of CD4+/CD8- T cells and CD3+ macrophages.

Interleukin-12 Gene Therapy

Interleukin-12 has been found to stimulate cytotoxic lymphocytes and NK cells. In preliminary studies, Tahara et al[61] demonstrated reduced tumorigenicity of murine melanoma cells when injected in a mixture with IL-12–producing NIH/3T3 fibroblasts into syngeneic mice.

Interferon Gene Therapy

As mentioned above, Rosenthal et al[49] demonstrated the rejection of murine fibrosarcoma (CMS-5) cells retrovirally transduced with IL-2 and IFN-γ or IFN-γ alone. The rejection of IL-2/IFN-γ–producing cells was CD8+ cytotoxic T-cell–mediated, while macrophages mediated rejection of CMS-5 cells transduced with

IFN-γ alone. A renal carcinoma cell line was also reported as having decreased tumorigenicity following transfection with IL-2 and/or IFN-α, even in T-cell–depleted mice.[50] Macrophages were found to be infiltrating the injection site.

Retroviral transduction of nonimmunogenic murine sarcoma cells with IFN-γ resulted in the upregulation of MHC class I antigens and generated CD8+ TILs, which were therapeutic against nontransduced tumor cells.[62] Similar results were reported following IL-2 or IFN-γ transduction of human melanoma and renal cancer cells.[63,64]

Mice that rejected IFN-γ–transduced murine neuroblastoma cells were found to be immune to a second tumor challenge.[65] Further, vaccination with IFN-γ–producing murine fibrosarcoma (MCA-101) cells resulted in a regression of established pulmonary tumor metastases of nonimmunogenic parental MCA-101 cells.[62]

Tumor Necrosis Factor Gene Therapy

After inserting the TNF gene into murine tumor cells, Teng et al[66] found that TNF-producing tumors exhibited decreased tumorigenicity in nude mice. Most of the mice injected with TNF-producing tumors did not exhibit the cachexia associated with TNF despite their having TNF levels that were antitumorigenic. Only one high-producing clone resulted in weight loss in the mice. These effects were reversible with the systemic administration of monoclonal antibody against TNF. Blankenstein et al[67] reported similar findings with TNF-transduced murine plasmacytoma cells injected into syngeneic mice. The immune response was found to be mediated by macrophages and was reversible with anti-type 3 complement receptor antibody, which inhibits macrophage migration. In contrast, the antitumor response against TNF-producing murine sarcoma (MCA-205) cells was shown to be absent in CD4+/CD8+ T cell–depleted mice.[68] Immunologically intact mice that rejected the TNF-producing cells were immune to rechallenge with nontransduced MCA-205 cells and manifested a lymphocytic infiltrate at the injection site.

Macrophage-Colony Stimulating Factor Gene Therapy

The human M-CSF gene has been inserted into a human ovarian cancer cell line. Injection of these transduced cells into nude mice resulted in an inverse correlation between M-CSF expression levels and tumorigenicity.[68]

Granulocyte-Colony Stimulating Factor Gene Therapy

Murine adenocarcinoma cells transduced with the granulocyte-colony stimulating factor gene demonstrate reduced tumorigenicity in syngeneic, NK cell–depleted, and athymic mice.[70] Delayed tumor growth also resulted after the injection of a mixture of transduced and nontransduced cells into the mice. Neutrophils were shown to comprise a majority of the cellular infiltrate at the tumor site.

MULTIPLE DRUG RESISTANCE GENE THERAPY

The multiple drug resistance gene (*MDR-1*) was discovered in tumor cells that were able to pump out a variety of chemothera-peutic drugs. The retrovirus-mediated ex vivo transduction of murine hematopoietic stem cells with the *MDR-1* gene resulted in protection of these cells in mice treated with high doses of paclitaxel.[71] Two clinical trials have been approved and another is pending approval to apply this strategy of bone marrow protection during high-dose chemotherapy of brain tumors, and disseminated breast and ovarian cancer.

References
1. Rosenberg SA, et al. *N Engl J Med* 1990;323:570-578.
2. Kasid A, et al. *Proc Natl Acad Sci USA* 1990;87:473-477.
3. Culver K, et al. *Proc Natl Acad Sci USA* 1991;88:3155-3159.
4. Anderson C. *Nature* 1992;360:399-400.
5. Marincola FM, et al. *J Immunol* 1994;152:3500-3513.
6. Rosenberg SA, et al. *Ann Surg* 1993;218:455-634.
7. Hwu P, et al. *J Immunol* 1993;150:4104-4115.
8. Hwu P, Rosenberg SA. *Cancer Detect Prevent* 1994;18:43-50.
9. Yannelli J, et al. *J Immunol Method* 1993;161:77-90.
10. Mitsudomi T, et al. *Cancer Res* 1991;51:4999-5002.
11. Gibbs J. *Semin Cancer Biol* 1992;6:383-390.
12. Zhang Y, et al. *Hum Gene Ther* 1993;4:451-460.
13. Georges RN, et al. *Cancer Res* 1993;53:1743-1746.
14. Kashani-Sabet M, et al. *Cancer Res* 1994;54:900-902.
15. Kashani-Sabet M, et al. *Antisense Res Develop* 1992;2:3-15.
16. Funato T, et al. *Adv Enzyme Regul* 1992;32:195-209.
17. Robinson-Benion C, et al. *Leukemia* 1994;8:S152-S155.
18. Fujiwara T, et al. *Cancer Res* 1993;53:4129-4133.
19. Chen YM, et al. *Oncogene* 1991;6:1799-1805.
20. Cai DW, et al. *Hum Gene Ther* 1993;4:617-624.
21. Fujiwara T, et al. *Cancer Res* 1994;54:2287-2291.
22. Goyette MC, et al. *Mol Cell Biol* 1992;12:1387-1395.
23. Leone A, et al. *Cell* 1991;65:25-35.
24. Barba D, et al. *J Neurosurg* 1993;79:729-735.
25. Oldfield EH, et al. *Hum Gene Ther* 1993;4:39-69.
26. Ram Z, et al. *Cancer Res* 1993;53:83-88.
27. Culver KW, et al. *Science* 1992;256:1550-1552.
28. Caruso M, et al. *Proc Natl Acad Sci USA* 1993;90:7024-7028.
29. Hasegawa Y, et al. *Am J Respir Cell Molec Biol* 1993;8:655-661.
30. Golumbek PT, et al. *J Immunotherapy* 1992;12:224-230.
31. Huber BE, et al. *Proc Natl Acad Sci USA* 1991;88:8039-8043.
32. Moolten FL, et al. *Hum Gene Ther* 1990;1:125-134.
33. Huber BE, et al. *Cancer Res* 1993;53:4619-4626.
34. Austin EA, Huber BE. *Molec Pharmacol* 1993;43:380-387.
35. Mullen CA, et al. *Proc Natl Acad Sci USA* 1992;89:33-37.
36. Mullen CA, et al. *Cancer Res* 1994;54:1503-1506.
37. Nabel GJ, et al. *Proc Natl Acad Sci USA* 1993;90:11307-11311.
38. Trojan J, et al. *Science* 1993;259:94-97.
39. Patel PM, et al. *J Immunother* 1993;14:310-313.
40. Schendel DJ, Gansbacher B. *Cancer Res* 1993;53:4020-4025.
41. Lotze MT, et al. *Hum Gene Ther* 1994;5:41-55.
42. Miller AR, et al. *Surg Forum* 1993;49:512-514.
43. Tsai SC, et al. *J Natl Cancer Inst* 1993;85:546-553.
44. Vieweg J, et al. *Cancer Res* 1994;54:1760-1765.
45. Gansbacher B, et al. *J Exp Med* 1990;172:1217-1224.
46. Karp SE, et al. *J Immunol* 1993;150:896-908.
47. Porgador A, et al. *Int J Cancer* 1993;53:471-477.
48. Visseren MJ, et al. *J Immunother Emphasis Tumor Immunol* 1994;15:119-128.
49. Rosenthal FM, et al. *Blood* 1994;83:1289-1298.

50. Belldegrun A, et al. *J Nat Cancer Inst* 1993;85:207-216.
51. Bannerji R, et al. *J Immunol* 1994;152:2324-2332.
52. Haddada H, et al. *Hum Gene Ther* 1993;4:703-711.
53. McBride WH, et al. *Folia Biologica (Praha)* 1994 (in press).
54. Golumbek PT, et al. *Science* 1991;254:713-716.
55. Tepper RI, et al. *Science* 1992;257:548-551.
56. Porgador A, et al. *Cancer Res* 1992;52:3679-3686.
57. Mullen CA, et al. *Cancer Res* 1992;52:6020-6024.
58. McBride WH, et al. *Cancer Res* 1992;52:3931-3937.
59. Miller AR, et al. *Blood* 1993;82:3686-3694.
60. Hock H, et al. *J Exp Med* 1991;174:1291-1298.
61. Tahara H, et al. Cancer Gene Therapy Using Interleukin-12. *Proc Society University Surgeons* 1993, p 154.
62. Restifo NP, et al. *J Exp Med* 1992;175:1423-1431.
63. Gastl G, et al. *Cancer Res* 1992;52:6229-6236.
64. Gansbacher B, et al. *Blood* 1992;80:2817-2825.
65. Watanabe Y, et al. *Proc Natl Acad Sci USA* 1989;86:9456.
66. Teng MN, et al. *Proc Natl Acad Sci USA* 1991;88:3535.
67. Blankenstein T, et al. *J Exp Med* 1991;173:1047-1052.
68. Asher AL, et al. *J Immunol* 1991;146:3227-3234.
69. Heike Y, et al. *Int J Cancer* 1993;54:851-857.
70. Colombo MP, et al. *J Exp Med* 1991;173:889-897.
71. Sorrentino BP, et al. *Science* 1992;257:99-103.

Index

Page numbers in **boldface** type refer to pages on which tables or figures appear; an *italic t* or *f* denotes tables or figures, respectively.